Praise for *Diversity in Cl*

"You won't find a more balanced and better written primer on multicultural awareness and diversity. Lambers Fisher writes like an engaging therapist who combines challenge, acceptance, and love."

— **William J. Doherty, PhD,** Professor and Director of the
Citizen Professional Center at the University of Minnesota

"In this work, Lambers brilliantly weaves together complex topics such as race relations, culture, social justice, and critical elements of developing trusting therapeutic relationships with diverse groups of clients. More importantly, perhaps, he offers the reader refreshingly optimistic, encouraging, and easily accessible insights and guidance regarding how to navigate such complexities in a respectful, thoughtful, humanistic, and uplifting way that validates all life stories and experiences."

— **Sean M. Reardon, PhD, LP,** Director of Outpatient
Behavioral Health, Park Nicollet Clinic

"Lambers delivers exactly what the title promises: a shame-free approach to increasing multicultural competency. He emphasizes competence as a journey of learning and growth with relatable anecdotes and thoughtful questions for ongoing reflection. This book was an incredibly easy read, especially for such challenging and often emotionally charged areas of consideration. If you've been confused or even offended by training efforts in diversity awareness in the past, consider this a breath of fresh air. Lambers makes clear the goal of meeting clients with empathy and respect rather than furthering polarization—and all while validating that multicultural competence is a journey, not a destination. This is a must-read for any helping professional wanting to grow in their understanding and effectiveness, and I will be recommending it to my non-professional friends as well!"

— **Jenny Beall, MA, LPCC,**
Threads of Hope Counseling

"In my over 35-year career in the human services field, Lambers is the finest trainer on cultural diversity and competency I have encountered, and I am thankful that he has captured his deep wisdom to share with helping professionals."

— **Tim Walsh, MA, LP, DPA,** Vice President of
Minnesota Adult and Teen Challenge

"*Diversity in Clinical Practice* is the how-to guide that needs to be on every culturally competent clinician's bookshelf! Lambers Fisher helps therapists get out of their own way by minimizing their own obstacles and replacing them with tangible abilities. This text empowers helpers and healers to integrate practical skills and ideas with their own hard-earned wisdom and experience. Do not miss this opportunity to do therapy better."

— **Samantha Zaid, PhD, Rev, LMFT,** Marriage & Family Therapy
Graduate Program Director, Saint Mary's University of Minnesota

"A thoughtful, comprehensive, and accessible guide on how to work with an array of diversity in a clinical setting, and a recommended reference source for one's office bookshelf. With truly shame-free education and compassionate direction, Lambers Fisher frees the clinician to expand their practice (and their world) to people who may be different from them in a variety of ways."

— **Aaron Testard, LMFT, LPCC,**
LGBTQ Mental Health Expert, Trainer, and Consultant

"Lambers's work deserves to be a standard in education for helping professionals. The book's research summaries make nuanced concepts clear, and the personal reflection questions provided make controversial issues humane. With the use of frameworks and a wide array of case vignettes, Lambers cultivates a commitment to diversity education in clinical practice that is integral to professional competence. No reader is left feeling this work is for 'someone else,' and each one will be a better professional (and human) for having read it."

— **Kelsey Crowe, PhD,** Author of *There Is No Good Card for This:*
What to Say and Do When Life Is Scary, Awful, and
Unfair to People You Love and Founder of Empathy Bootcamp

"With a tone of acceptance, grace, and guidance permeating throughout, Lambers has poured his heart and soul into this easy-to-follow and incredibly meaningful book. Lambers establishes a lens through which to approach situations and creates space for the reader to process the content as they read. It is more than an informative book, it's also a workbook in many respects. Knowledge + Action = Change. Cultural competency is a daunting aspiration, and Lambers has done a remarkable job of understanding where readers at every level are coming from and helping them enrich their relationships professionally and personally."

— **Rebecca Hustad, MS, LMFT**
Beacon Mental Health Resources

"In this book, *Diversity in Clinical Practice*, Lambers Fisher invites readers into honest reflection on important cultural issues that influence our macro and micro experiences and offers many practical applications to support forward movement toward cultural responsiveness. As an educator and therapist, I have engaged with many resources, and this is one of the best for understanding diversity in all its many splendored dimensions, for highlighting ways to grow and develop in one's own cultural awareness and responsiveness, and for practical applications that can be engaged immediately. This is a superb resource for all helping professionals!"

— **Tina Watson Wiens, MA,** Assistant Professor, Clinical Supervisor, and Marriage & Family Therapy Program Director, Bethel Seminary

"*Diversity in Clinical Practice* educates your mind, transforms your heart, and models responsible action. Filled with comprehensive vocabulary lessons, journal activities for deeper engagement with the material, and case vignettes, this book a must for all clinicians, leaders, and clergy. Lambers shows us how to take wise, brave, and loving responsibility for inclusion without using shame or guilt"

— **Traci Ruble, MFT,** Director of Sidewalk Talk Community Listening Project

"All helpers need this basic primer to guide them into greater competency and cultural sensitivity."

— **Dr. Clifford and Joyce Penner,** authors of *The Gift of Sex*

"Lambers has a uniquely relatable way of discussing polarizing and potentially divisive cultural experiences in ways that makes you feel comfortable... that is no easy feat. The way he explains situations makes the reader feel empowered to 'lean in' to uncomfortable cross-cultural encounters by offering practical strategies and guidance. This book is a must-read for any conscientious clinician who wants to deepen their work, in a way that makes others feel seen and valued no matter their similarities or differences."

— **Elizabeth Irias, LMFT,** President & Founder of Clearly Clinical

DIVERSITY
in Clinical Practice

A Practical & Shame-Free Guide to Reducing
Cultural Offenses & Repairing Cross-Cultural Relationships

Lambers Fisher, MS, LMFT, MDIV

Copyright © 2021 Lambers Fisher
Published by
PESI Publishing
3839 White Ave
Eau Claire, WI 54703

Cover: Amy Rubenzer
Editing: Jenessa Jackson, PhD, and Lauren Hovde
Layout: Amy Rubenzer & Bookmasters
ISBN: 9781683733881

PESI Publishing
pesipublishing.com

ABOUT THE AUTHOR

Lambers Fisher is a licensed marriage and family therapist who received his professional training at Fuller Theological Seminary, a school with a fully accredited School of Psychology alongside its School of Theology. As he began to recognize the need for quality mental health services, he found that many individuals in his community maintained a stigma around mental health services, preferring instead to seek spiritual help through their local churches. Therefore, he also received a Master of Divinity so he could provide support both in the psychology field and in the church environments. His Master of Marriage and Family Therapy gives him credibility for those cautious of pastoral counseling efforts, while his Master of Divinity gives him credibility for those uncomfortable with secular psychology. This combination has opened the door for Fisher to offer balanced, yet effective, services to those who need it but who would, for various reasons, otherwise not receive it.

Over the past 18 years, Fisher has had the pleasure of providing counseling services in a variety of different environments, including urban and suburban environments, non-profit and for-profit settings, small group practices, large mental health agencies, and secular and Christian environments. As part of his counseling roles, he has conducted pastoral counseling and served as the Director of Counseling at a large metropolitan church. He currently supervises aspiring therapists, is an adjunct instructor, and provides trainings for mental health professionals across the country. He has had the pleasure of providing counseling services to a large variety of individuals, couples, and families.

In addition to his professional experiences, Fisher has had the opportunity to travel internationally. He participated in a foreign exchange program while in high school, which sent him to France twice and to Germany once, and he participated in a mission trip to Nigeria prior to beginning graduate school. As a part of these programs, he was able to experience different cultures firsthand, and he saw that we often have more in common than we have differences. He began to see how his actions, and the actions of those around him, were influenced more by assumptions—both negative and positive—than by knowledge. He would like to share the knowledge, experiences, and perspectives he has gained to help enhance and expand your view of culture. Hopefully, it will help you have a greater impact on those you encounter.

TABLE OF CONTENTS

ACKNOWLEDGMENTS

Thanks...

    To my wife for her continued support and belief in me.

    To my family for always encouraging me to be my best.

    To my clients for trusting me to understand and help them and for being patient as I learned how to do it better.

    To PESI for providing me the opportunity to meet professionals from around the country, to share numerous experiences, and to receive feedback that has enhanced the quality of this book.

    To the mental health professionals and colleagues who have attended my national seminars and have helped me continually gain a greater understanding of a variety of cultural experiences.

INTRODUCTION

What Makes This Different from Other Books on Diversity?

This book is inspired by the many individuals, professional and non-professional alike, who have shied away from other books, courses, and seminars on the topic of multicultural awareness and diversity. Many individuals have expressed a desire to attend a training on this topic only to find the material presented in a way that created feelings of shame, guilt, and fear. Others have expressed that the information presented was so deep and focused on the history of various cultural groups that they left with an appreciation for people different than themselves, but they also felt more incompetent, as the information simply highlighted how much they didn't know.

In light of such experiences, the goal of this book is to offer a balanced, practical, and applicable perspective on this topic and to help you feel more confident and competent on matters of multicultural awareness and diversity. I hope to provide insights that you can put into practice immediately and that equip you to reduce cultural barriers, misunderstandings, and offenses so you can have better relationships with those from a greater variety of cultural backgrounds.

Who Should Read This Book?

Although the language in this book is primarily geared toward mental health professionals seeking to build better therapeutic rapport with their clients, it is also applicable to a wide range of individuals beyond the counseling profession, including:

- *Medical professionals* interested in strategies for improving their bedside manner and for avoiding communication barriers that can limit treatment effectiveness
- *Educators and administrators* desiring to help students feel respected and understood in consideration of their cultural differences and uniqueness rather than in spite of them
- *Business leaders* motivated to reach out to new and existing clients in a way that helps them feel like valued customers, making efforts to learn about their needs and meeting a greater variety of needs in their community
- *Religious leaders* hoping to convey their desire to understand and accept people's differences while making efforts to meet spiritual and emotional needs

- *Politicians and community leaders* faced with changing demographics and limited expertise but who have a sincere motivation to help create healthy community interactions and bring about positive change
- *Law enforcement professionals* seeking to improve public perceptions, cultivate genuine interactions, and make effective decisions for their own safety, as well as the safety and well-being of the communities they protect
- *Anyone* who wants to confront fear and discomfort stemming from lack of knowledge and learn how to effectively interact with people who are different

Why Read This Book

Many White helping professionals feel scared or ignorant. I began training therapists on the topic of multicultural awareness and diversity while I was employed at a large counseling agency, which had some ethnic diversity but consisted predominately of White mental health professionals. One of the leaders of that agency had the idea to create a training series for therapists where they would utilize existing therapists with particular strengths to provide the training. It began with finding someone who was good with assessments, another therapist who was great with ethics, another who was good with crisis management, and so on. When leaders asked, "Who can we get to do a training on multicultural awareness and diversity?" the brainstorming stalled. Why? Because most therapists concluded that they knew some, but not enough, on what is commonly considered a very sensitive topic to teach without offending others.

They'd say things like "I don't have a lot of experience working with *this* population," "I don't know how to meet the needs of *that* population," "I don't have enough diverse experiences," "I don't want to accidentally offend others while trying to help," or "What can I possibly say that can help others if I'm not a cultural expert?" After a while, I volunteered my services. Not because I considered myself an expert on every culture—far from it, actually. Rather, I felt that I knew enough to be able to help those who felt either too afraid or too ignorant to act.

When I began providing training for therapists at that large counseling agency, it became clear that many minority counselors assumed their minority status was synonymous with diversity awareness or competence. I would casually check in with colleagues to see if they would be attending an upcoming training, and sometimes the response from therapists of color would be a very sincere and disinterested "Nope." When I curiously followed up and asked why, they would tilt their heads and open their hands as if to say, "Isn't it obvious?" What they were doing was nonverbally referencing their visibly evident ethnic minority status as the obvious reason why they didn't need to attend a training on multicultural awareness and diversity.

My response to these messages was to point out that there is more to cultural awareness than having the experience of one type of minority group. Being part of an ethnic minority doesn't make someone knowledgeable about other cultures involving different genders, sexual orientations, ages, abilities, religious beliefs, socioeconomic statuses, and more. We can all benefit from increasing our competence through the lessons learned from others' experiences.

Cultural misunderstandings negatively impact our clients. Too often, it is our clients who feel oppressed or misunderstood, avoid counseling altogether, or leave counseling early due to unintentional and avoidable cultural misunderstandings. Can we reasonably expect to know everything all the time? Not at all. Neither can we rest in hope that as long as we don't *intend* to offend then it won't feel offensive to our clients. Ignorance is not bliss; we have an ethical and professional responsibility to accept that we don't know everything, to value what we do know, and to make the most of every opportunity to learn more.

What This Book Is *Not*

A history lesson. In order to make this book practical and usable for you as soon as possible, I will focus on the present and how to practically engage with diversity today.

A politics debate. Another reason people often shy away from the topic of cultural diversity is that people tend to have very strong feelings about one side of the argument versus another, often sparking controversy or debate. As therapists, we are often tasked with helping people wrestle with controversial feelings, no matter what side of the controversy they (or we) are on. Therefore, I will address a variety of topics in this book, many of which may be considered controversial. However, I will make every effort to discuss each topic in a way that focuses less on the absolute rightness or wrongness of the topics and instead on the varied legitimate feelings and perspectives of the individuals who express them. Hence the lack of need for debate. You need to be able to understand both sides of any argument—whether you agree with it or not—and I will explore how to do so effectively and professionally.

An exhaustive "everything you need to know about" cheat sheet or stereotype list. This book doesn't have a chapter on every possible cultural group with all of the essential facts you'll need to know about them. Instead of providing a lot of information about a few cultural groups, this book will provide specifically chosen perspectives on a number of cultural groups. More importantly, I will discuss practical strategies you can utilize to help others from various cultural groups.

A cultural-specific diagnostic and treatment plan. It would probably be very convenient if I were able to tell you, "Whenever you meet a new client from *this* or *that* cultural group, and you get to the point in your initial assessment when you need to determine an appropriate diagnosis, open your DSM-5 and turn to these pages to find all the diagnoses that apply to that cultural group." Although that would save a lot of professional effort, it does not work that way—not with diagnostic assessments and not with treatment plans. Being a part of a cultural group doesn't determine one's diagnoses, though certain cultural experiences can influence verbal, behavioral, or emotional symptom expression. And the more you know about various cultural experiences, values, and ways of being, the more competent and effective you can become at helping identify the source of clients' struggles, as well as appropriate solutions to those struggles.

A cultural guilt trip. Many people have conveyed their caution about reading books like this or about attending seminars on this topic because the authors or speakers spend most of the time saying things like "I shouldn't have to say this, but…" or "You should already know this by now, but…" That approach tends to make people feel ashamed and guilty. I believe that we have all learned what we know from the experiences we have been fortunate to have. Yet we have not all had the same opportunities to learn. It is pointless to shame someone for their lack of opportunity.

What You *Can* Expect from This Book

Breadth (versus depth). In order to make this book as practical and immediately useful as possible, I will try to briefly address many relevant topics related to multicultural awareness and diversity. Each of the areas covered in this book could justifiably fill its own book, seminar, or graduate course. Therefore, if at any point you find yourself yearning for more information or practical tools on a particular cultural topic, I encourage you to seek out books and seminars on that topic for greater edification.

Increased understanding of diversity and competence. There is a lot of misunderstanding regarding what diversity and competence mean. I will recommend ways to understand key words that can help you communicate more effectively.

Increased knowledge of self and others. Cultural competence involves increasing knowledge and awareness of others, as well as oneself. Simply put, the more you understand about who you are, the better you can understand the ways in which you are similar or dissimilar to others.

Enhanced perspective and empathy for other cultures. As your understanding of yourself and others grows, so can your capacity for empathy for the perspectives and experiences of others.

Increased confidence. It is my hope that as a result of reading this book, you feel more prepared and confident in your ability to serve clients who are culturally different than yourself.

Increased knowledge base. Our personal experiences and the experiences of those around us are our starting point for building upon what we already know.

A Reasonable Cultural Competence Goal

With respect to identifying a reasonable personal goal for cultivating cultural competence, I recommend that you consider the following three guiding principles:

- **Learn to accept the inevitability of offense.** No matter how much you learn about yourself or others, I do not believe that you can completely avoid cultural offenses. There are simply too many people in this world to learn it all. And even when you learn about a group of people, over time you discover that not everyone in a group is the same, and the rules you learned can change over time. This truth can help reduce the shame and guilt at not being able to meet the unreasonable prerequisite of exhaustive cultural knowledge. Instead, accept that despite our best efforts, unavoidable offenses will occasionally occur.

- **Make intentional efforts to reduce the frequency of the offenses that will inevitably occur.** You can begin to appreciate what you do know and use your growing knowledge to improve the quality of your cross-cultural interactions. For some, seeing your imperfect effort to try to avoid cultural offenses may help reduce the likelihood that something will be experienced as offensive.

- **Make intentional efforts to repair relationships damaged by cultural offenses.** When cultural offenses occur, you can employ specific strategies to repair the damage and reassure your clients of your openness and willingness to take steps to make future experiences together better.

---

3 Reasonable Cultural Competence Goals

- Accept the Inevitability of Offense
- Reduce the Frequency of Offenses
- Repair Relationships Damaged by Offenses

Too often, well-intentioned helping professionals conclude that their lack of cultural knowledge and diverse experiences make the goal of effective multicultural awareness and competence futile. They perceive insurmountable barriers between their genuine intent and their goals of healthy cross-cultural relationship interactions. However, I believe that there are practical strategies that you can employ immediately to create a significant and positive impact on those you encounter personally and professionally—no matter how many cultural similarities or differences there may be between you. **You don't need to know everything about everyone in order to have a positive impact on someone.** By building upon skills you already possess and by incorporating new strategies, we will build a foundation that you can put into practice immediately, helping you strengthen your personal and professional cross-cultural relationships for years to come.

Why Should We Increase Our Cultural Competence?

The world is changing. Not only is the world changing, but the country is changing. Maybe even your city, community, or family are changing. As demographics continually change, the people you encounter on a daily basis change as well. Whether it's increased varieties of ethnic groups, increased freedoms for individuals to express their gender and sexual orientation, varying political beliefs, or differing rural versus urban values, things are slowly changing, and we need to be able to adjust to those changes.

Our comfort zones must expand. Since the world is continually changing, we don't have the luxury to stay within our comfort zone. Sure, we all have a comfort zone, and that's okay. But if your comfort zone is so small that it limits whom you can help and how much you can help, then it is your responsibility to grow as the opportunity arises.

I like to think of it like a playground game of tag. You begin with a home base, where you're safe. Then when the opportunity arises, you run around a bit, and then you run back to your safe home base. Similarly, I think it's perfectly healthy to have a personal and professional home base—things you experience as normal, comfortable, and easy. However, every once in a while, I believe that it is beneficial to branch out of what is comfortable and easy and to try something new. Learn about someone else, take a healthy interest in someone else's normal, and make efforts to meet the needs of someone new to you.

There is no need to feel pressure to learn everything about everyone. That would be impossible. After all, no matter how large you expand your comfort zone, there will still be something outside of it. So learn to accept the benefits of your comfort zone—your scope of competence—and then make the most of opportunities to expand it.

Professional bubbles no longer match clientele. There once was a time when professionals could operate in a professional bubble. Many times, this bubble was created very unintentionally: "I don't mean to operate in a professional bubble. I just happen to work in this certain suburb, which has a large percentage of this certain population, which tends to have a particular need that I have become very good at addressing. So I don't really have to expand beyond this bubble or my professional comfort zone." In one sense, that perspective has merit. However, in another sense, that perspective has significant limitations. Even if you are able to stay in the comfort zone of your professional bubble, despite the changing world around you, the reality is that your clients do not live in that same professional bubble. To remain effective at helping your clients live in a diverse world, it behooves you to branch out and to get to know that world outside of your comfort zone.

We have an ethical mandate to maintain cultural competence. Most professional licensing boards—including, but not limited to, boards of psychology,[1] marriage and family therapy,[2] social work,[3] and counseling[4]—have published ethical codes of conduct, which at the very least have some type of disclaimer discouraging discrimination based on factors such as race, age, ethnicity, culture, color, socioeconomic status, mental or physical disability, language, gender, health status, religion, national origin, immigration status, political belief, sexual orientation, gender identity, or relationship status. This is the minimum standard. However, shouldn't our goal be to exceed this standard? Shouldn't we go beyond *not discriminating* and learn to appreciate different experiences, identities, and perspectives? I believe this extra step is a significant step on the journey toward increased cultural competence.

Cultural competence leads to greater client satisfaction and rapport. Making the effort to understand and help your clients feel understood is one of the core components of building therapeutic rapport. We can accomplish that task by making efforts to understand our clients' presenting struggles, as well as their personal experiences and the culture in which they have developed and are learning to overcome those struggles.

Cultural competence enhances our professional effectiveness. Building healthy therapeutic rapport not only helps increase client satisfaction, but it is also correlated with increased therapeutic effectiveness. When a client feels understood by their therapist, they are more likely to be receptive to therapeutic insights and challenges and more compliant with treatment strategies and recommendations. This ultimately leads to improved treatment outcomes.

Ignorance is not bliss. Some therapists assume that as long as they have good intentions, they don't need to learn about others' experiences and how those experiences are similar to or different than their own. They believe that trying their best to avoid things that seem offensive is enough. Their sincere hope is that what they don't know can't hurt them. More importantly, they hope that their ignorance won't hurt their clients. Unfortunately, this hope to prevent harm, in the face of ignorance, actually contributes to unintentional harm to clients, and it occurs in a relationship context that was supposed to be a safe place.

---

[1] American Psychological Association. (2017). *Ethical principles of psychologists and code of conduct.* https://www.apa.org/ethics/code

[2] American Association for Marriage and Family Therapy. (2015). *AAMFT code of ethics.* https://www.aamft.org/Legal_Ethics/Code_of_Ethics.aspx

[3] National Association of Social Workers. (2017). *NASW code of ethics.* https://www.socialworkers.org/About/Ethics/Code-of-Ethics/Code-of-Ethics-English

[4] National Board for Certified Counselors. (2016). *NBCC code of ethics.* https://www.nbcc.org/Assets/Ethics/NBCCCodeofEthics.pdf

No matter how egalitarian you may consider yourself to be in your therapeutic role, you would do well to not take for granted the therapeutic authority inherent in that relationship. Just as you have the power to significantly help your clients, you also have the power to significantly harm your clients. Even if you don't have a negative tone, attitude, or intention, unintentional offenses and oppression, invalidated feelings, and identity trauma can occur at any time. I will explore several ways to reduce the unintentionally negative impact we may have on clients.

Graduate programs offer limited professional training. Whether you have been a licensed professional practicing for decades or whether the ink on your license is still wet, we can all benefit from increased knowledge and understanding of various cultural groups. Studies have shown that academic programs often focus too much on research and not enough on practical application.

I was trained to have a great appreciation for the role of research and evidence-based practices. However, the vast majority of graduate training programs for mental health professionals (and many other professional training programs as well) could improve their efforts to prepare students to serve effectively in a culturally diverse world. There is often a lot more emphasis put on history and theory and less on practical tools, strategies, and understanding of the diverse and changing needs of real people today. If you feel as though everyone else learned more about cultural competency than you did in graduate school, you are not alone in that feeling, and you're likely incorrect.

Professionals are limited by their personal experience. So if we all haven't been trained to be experts in cultural competency, then what are we left with? Well, without sufficient training, we are left to rely on our own personal experiences. Unfortunately, many of us conclude that we haven't had enough diverse experiences to even come close to being sufficiently competent in understanding or meeting the needs of individuals, couples, or families from other cultural backgrounds. As you will hear repeatedly throughout this book, I do not believe that this dilemma has to be the end of our story. You likely have more resources than you think to get started, and we will explore some strategies to enhance what you have.

An isolated therapy field increases the likelihood that therapists will remain in their comfort zone. Some of you happen to work in teaching clinics or organizations where therapeutic services are provided in a room that also has a two-way mirror, where a small group or class sits on the other side for consultation or educational purposes. For the rest of us, counseling services are completely confidential and private. On the one hand, this confidentiality provides ethical and emotional safety for our clients. On the other hand, it has the unintended and unfortunate consequence of creating an isolating environment for therapists, often with minimal support. Outside of supervision received prior to licensure and voluntary consultation received after licensure, therapists are often left alone, with little accountability and minimal encouragement as it relates to branching out from their comfort zone and becoming more culturally competent.

Practically speaking, only you and your client will know how culturally competent and considerate you really are—and since, in many cases, you are the first and only helping professional your client has ever worked with, then only you really know how good you are at this. This is not something to be taken lightly, as this is a very big responsibility we have, not only to our clients, but also to ourselves: to make sure that we are handling clients' concerns and emotions with care.

Knowledge and experience are both essential. As we wrestle with the dilemma of limited knowledge—alongside limited experience related to cultural experiences other than our own—a common question arises: Which one is more important? Knowledge or experience? Interestingly, research shows it is personal experience *combined with* education and diversity training that results in higher cultural competency (Ponterotto et al., 2000). Whether it's through the experiences you have had yourself or the awareness-producing moments you have experienced vicariously through family and friends, these can be combined with professional trainings to enhance your diversity competence. They need not be separated or prioritized.

If you focus on one and minimize the other (e.g., "I don't need to interact with others because I have read about them and taken a course" or "What can a class or book teach me? I know everything I need to know from my personal experiences"), you are limiting your capacity for understanding. Can you still be effective? Sure. However, you can be even more effective if you find a way to increase the lessons you've learned from your personal life *and* your educational experiences. Whatever area you personally have more of, consider that your strength. And whatever area you have less of, consider that your targeted growth area. Use what you have as a starting point and grow from it, one opportunity and experience at a time.

Multicultural competence is synonymous with general counseling competence. Many wonder whether or not multicultural competence even needs to be a priority for those not working with a high percentage of individuals from minority backgrounds. Research on this topic suggests that not only is multicultural competence relevant to everyone, but the presence of multicultural competence is synonymous with general counseling competence (Coleman, 1998).

Put another way, you cannot say, "I'm a great counselor, I just don't do that multicultural stuff" or "I'm a great counselor, I just don't work with kids, women, and clients over 65 years of age." Multicultural counseling need not be a specialty or niche. In order to be a generally competent counselor, you would do well to learn how to apply your knowledge and skills to the greatest variety of clients you may possibly encounter.

Cultural awareness influences assessment and diagnosis. Whether or not you embrace the task of completing assessments and making diagnoses, mental health professionals have a responsibility to accurately assess and diagnose client struggles in order to provide effective client care. Because varying cultural experiences and understandings can impact the effectiveness of those assessments, insufficient diversity training can unintentionally influence those assessments in a negative way.

Contrary to popular belief, the *Diagnostic and Statistical Manual of Mental Disorders* (DSM; APA, 2013) is not the mental health Bible. As essential as it may be in the evaluation of client struggles, considering the DSM the mental health Bible tends to give it too much gravitas and skews its more practical usage. Instead, I like to think of it as a mental health checklist. It is a really big book of well-researched mental health–related symptoms, categorized by titles (i.e., diagnoses). The titles also need to be realized for what they are. They are not declarative labels or brands to be tattooed on our clients' foreheads as if to summarize the totality of who a person is. Rather, they are simply the shorthand words used to describe the symptoms the clients are struggling with. These shorthands are beneficial in that they point clinicians to the treatment plans that research has shown to be effective in reducing the symptoms associated with that diagnosis.

In short, accurate evaluation leads to accurate diagnoses, which leads to accurate treatment strategies and hopefully to reduced symptoms and positive client outcomes. If that is the case, what happens when reasonable and common cultural misunderstandings negatively influence that process?

Cultural competence decreases the likelihood of inaccurate evaluation, incorrect diagnosis, and poor treatment outcomes. Inaccurate evaluation can disrupt the assessment, diagnosis, and treatment process from the very beginning. Missing, ignoring, or minimizing relevant cultural factors that contribute to accurate symptom evaluation can skew your perspective and treatment direction. For example, are the behaviors you are hearing about really indicative of oppositional defiant disorder, or are those same behaviors more indicative of a difficulty adjusting to and coping with a transition from one culture to another?

Are you expected to know the full impact of every client's experience? That would be unreasonable. Subtle influencing factors like these can admittedly be difficult to see reliably, even for a trained professional. However, they are even more difficult to see if you're not even looking for them. **Therefore, it is critical that you intentionally look for potentially significant cultural influences during the assessment process and throughout the course of a therapeutic relationship.**

If we unintentionally fall victim to inaccurate symptom evaluation, then we will naturally formulate inaccurate diagnoses when consulting with the mental health checklist. And since the primary value in an accurate diagnostic label is to point us to the most appropriate treatment strategies, inaccurate diagnosis prevents us from developing appropriate and effective treatment strategies. Not only are ineffective treatment strategies inconvenient because they delay progress in reducing clients' undesired symptoms, but they can also contribute to long-term trauma for our clients.

Use the following worksheet to reflect on the ways in which you can step outside of your own comfort zone to become more informed on issues related to multicultural diversity.

Cultural Competency Journey Reflection

What type of clientele do I consider to be within my professional comfort zone?

_____

_____

_____

_____

In what ways can I step outside of my professional comfort zone today?

_____

_____

_____

_____

What opportunities are available to me to gain more diverse professional knowledge and/or experiences?

_____

_____

_____

_____

Progressing from Ignorance to Competence

Over the course of this book, I will explore multiple topics related to multicultural awareness and the practical application of such in your daily professional life. In order to set a foundation for the practical application of these strategies, I believe it would be beneficial to provide an overview of some research perspectives regarding how we develop and progress in our multicultural awareness and competence (e.g., Atkinson et al., 1993; Carney & Kahn, 1984; Priest, 1994; Sabnani et al., 1991). According to these models, we develop cultural competence by moving through a series of stages, beginning with ethnocentrism and ultimately progressing to cultural advocacy. However, it is important to note that these developmental stages are not intended to convey the exact process by which everyone develops cultural competence. Rather, the goal is to gain a greater appreciation for common processes people experience on their way to greater multicultural awareness and diversity competence. I'll discuss each of these stages in greater detail in the following section.

Ethnocentrism

Research suggests that we all start off life influenced by a certain degree of ethnocentrism. Many unfortunately believe that ethnocentrism is the same as negative, prejudiced, or racist thoughts. **On the contrary, ethnocentrism involves seeing the world a certain way based on one's personal experiences, rather than realizing there is a world with differing experiences outside of the way in which one has grown accustomed.** In thinking about ethnocentrism, I am reminded of the quote "A fish doesn't know it lives in water until it jumps out." It's less about having a negative view of others and others' experiences as it is about the fact that our reality is the only reality we know. Some people we encounter act in ways that reflect their minimal knowledge of various other cultural experiences. What is key is that they don't yet know what they don't know. It's a degree of ignorance that simply reflects a lack of knowledge. Their actions and interactions are led by their own ethnocentrism.

Diversity Denial

Slightly different from ethnocentrism is diversity denial, in which some people acknowledge differences in cultural experiences but deny that they hold any significant difference in how we interact with others. It is almost as if there is a sincere belief that everyone is basically the same, as if there are no differences among people that are significant enough to preclude well-intentioned efforts from being effective across cultures. Unfortunately, research has shown that well-intentioned efforts are not enough to replace increased multicultural awareness and competence.

Initial Awareness

A step closer to increased cultural competence occurs when people become aware of and accept their ethnocentrism (i.e., their cultural ignorance, lack of knowledge, etc.). In other words, they are like a fish that jumps out of water, falls back in the fishbowl, and in shock asks, "What was that?" When people are confronted with new and unexpected experiences, not only does this force them to make room for the existence of these experiences, but it also leads them to reevaluate their understanding of the only world they have ever known in a new way.

This stage is the beginning of learning. You may encounter people who do not know as much as would be beneficial, but at least they are aware of their ignorance. They accept that the world as they know it is not the same as others experience it, and they are willing to take steps to learn more and decrease that cultural ignorance. This increased awareness can be accomplished by making the most of opportunities to learn about the similarities and differences between various cultures.

Increased Self-Awareness

In order for people to effectively increase their awareness of the ways in which they are similar to or different from others, it is beneficial to increase their awareness of their own cultural identity. Doing so allows them to better know what they are comparing the outside world to. This may seem unnecessary or as if it should be obvious. However, it is one thing to realize that people from different cultural backgrounds do certain things differently and another thing to go the extra step to learn *why* they do those things that way. And it can only be a true comparison if people also learn why they themselves do things the way they do. In doing this, lessons can be learned about cultural motivations and values.

Internal Conflict

As ignorance decreases and awareness increases, individuals begin to learn about experiences other than their own and realize the impact their ignorance can have (and likely has had) on others. This can result in an internal conflict where individuals wrestle with two competing realizations. On the one hand, they have the genuine desire to interact with others well and hope that "as long as I'm not trying to hurt anybody, then everything and everyone will be fine." On the other hand, they have now learned that good intentions can have unintentional negative effects.

Some respond to this conflict by downplaying the importance of their ignorance, expressing things like "Look I tried, but this is just the way I am." Others acknowledge that good intentions are beneficial but not sufficient in and of themselves, leading to a growing drive to reduce the unintentionally negative impact of their ignorance and convey a genuine desire to grow in their cultural appreciation and understanding of others.

WAS IT TOO MUCH?

Consider... a man with White parents from a predominately White community. As he begins to reduce his ignorance and grow in his understanding of similarities and differences within his cultural group, as well as with other cultural groups, he also begins to see some inequalities. It becomes clear that many, though not all, who share his cultural identification have negative views about others that he does not share. An internal conflict arises where this man feels torn between the aspects of his culture that he identifies with and the aspects he does not identify with. It is especially disturbing when he realizes that others of the same cultural identity may come to believe that he shares the same negative cultural beliefs about others. The challenge for this individual then becomes, "What should I do about this? How do I reconcile these conflicting views of my cultural identity and my desire for healthy interactions with those from other cultural backgrounds?"

This particular individual concluded that the best way to show support for other cultures was to denounce his own cultural group's behavioral history and to support marginalized groups—so much so that he almost identified more with marginalized groups than he did with his own cultural group. This resulted in his speaking differently, dressing differently, and so on. His intended message was "I see the insensitivity of those who look like me, and I do not share those negative beliefs."

Unfortunately, cultural immersion gestures like these are not universally accepted as intended. For this individual, this grand shift in allegiance was not well received from individuals in the diverse community. They responded with messages like "You say you feel like one of us, but your experiences, perspectives, and privileges in this country reveal that you are not like us in many ways that count, and your efforts to suggest otherwise make us feel patronized and mocked rather than flattered by your imitation."

What followed was a backpedaling of sorts, in which he retreated back into his previously identified cultural expression but without the same ignorance. Eventually, he developed a healthy appreciation of the similarities across groups, along with an acceptance of his own cultural identity without the need to identify with every aspect of it.

Appreciation of Diversity

Just as individuals can wrestle with the internal conflict regarding the impact of their own ignorance, they can also experience an external conflict as they wrestle with increased awareness of cultural differences. With new knowledge comes a new responsibility to use that knowledge well and to enhance relationships rather than hurt them. As a result, increased cultural awareness can be very inconvenient.

As an individual increases their awareness, a transition can also occur where they develop a healthy appreciation for similarities and differences among people. When this occurs, people no longer view cultural differences as inconvenient things that they must learn and acknowledge but, rather, as traits that have both pros and cons. Instead of being perceived as barriers, differences are seen as unique characteristics that can aid individuals in offering creative contributions to their home, community, or work environments. In businesses, families, and communities, when those making decisions have largely similar experiences, there is often less diversity in thought, leading to more of the same rather than creative ideas for growth. However, these same groups thrive when there are a variety of perspectives that contribute to problem-solving and new ideas; this occurs more often when people with diverse life experiences are welcomed and appreciated so their unique perspectives can contribute to everyone's well-being.

Increased Accountability

It is not sufficient to simply hope that other people will see our reasonable intentions at multicultural competence and that these intentions will pacify hurt feelings and experiences of unintentional offense. Instead, we must take a proactive approach to this internal conflict by assuming responsibility for our actions. While it is not healthy to take responsibility for others' feelings, we can choose to care about how we have impacted others, and we can make intentional efforts to learn about the experiences, needs, and comfort zones of those from similar and differing backgrounds. This reduces the potentially negative impact of our ignorance and increases our willingness to modify our actions to benefit others.

Cultural Advocacy

As we become more comfortable with our increased self-awareness and other-awareness, we often experience discomfort when we see or hear about other people being negatively impacted by someone else's ethnocentrism or cultural ignorance. One way to be a part of the solution to this problem is to discover a personal style of advocating for the rights and appropriate treatment of others.

This does not necessarily involve advocating in the legal sense of the word. Rather, in clinical settings, it can refer to the selection of appropriate treatment strategies and other clinical recommendations. Without leaving the therapy room, advocacy can include helping your client see someone else's perspective, giving others the benefit of the doubt, and helping them interact with others in their environment and community in healthier ways. This advocacy is motivated by your increased knowledge and awareness of the needs and experiences of others, especially regarding the ways in which injustices and inequalities can be changed. It involves taking your increased knowledge and awareness and applying it to areas of need within your scope of practice and competence.

Using the Stages to Understand Others' Behaviors

These developmental models are not presented in order to convey a belief that everyone progresses through these stages in a specific linear manner—as if you'll be able to look at or listen to someone and say, "Ah, you must be in *this* stage." Rather, it is to broaden your awareness to the varying degrees of cultural-identity development and awareness and their potential impact on individual action. The more you understand, the greater your cultural grace and empathy becomes. You will be better able to advocate appropriately and help your clients make healthy, culturally considerate changes when necessary.

RECONCILING CONFLICTING CULTURAL VALUES AND NORMS

Consider... the experience of a young woman from a Hispanic background, whose parents legally brought their family to America to give their children a better chance to succeed. One day, this young woman expresses to her parents, "I appreciate the example you modeled for me and the values you instilled about working hard to provide for your family, but I have noticed that you and many people who look like us have the 'working hard' part down but haven't seemed to meet the standard for success that other people have. I have some school friends whose parents look like they have succeeded—who happen to be White Americans. And they say that if I learn to speak like them, dress like them, go to the same schools, get the same degrees, and advance in the same careers as them, then I too can succeed. So, Mom and Dad, I hope you don't mind—I don't mean anything against you—but I'm going to leave behind your ways of doing things and learn their ways so I can succeed in this country and provide better opportunities for my children."

With sincere motives, hopes, and expectations, this young woman then sets off to reap the benefits of conformity. However, it soon becomes apparent that the things that apply to her friends do not apply to her. She begins to think, *I don't understand. I did what my friends said. I learned to speak and dress like them. Although we got the same grades in high school, I didn't get accepted into as many colleges. I graduated with the degree they said I should get—and my academic achievements exceeded that of my co-applicants—but I was continually told that I "didn't fit what the employers were looking for" as they accepted someone else for the position. When I finally did get a job, the upward mobility for me was far slower than it was for others despite my undeniable hard work. There were wage gaps and a glass ceiling that didn't apply to my friends and to others who looked like them. I am beginning to wonder whether I made a mistake.*

After a genuine effort to reconcile conflicting cultural values and norms, some choose what seems to work, only to realize that it doesn't work the same for everyone. This often results in a revisiting of what was left behind with a greater appreciation for the pros and cons of their culture of origin, as well as the learned culture.

Cultural Competency Development in Practice

We are not all at the same stage of development as it relates to cultural self-awareness or other-awareness. When you come to this realization and recognize the ways in which you and others can grow, you can begin to understand why people might behave and express themselves in certain ways. If a client says something that seems skewed, before you react from a place characterized simply by the contrast between their perspective and yours, it may benefit you to take a step back and see if you can assess where the client is in their development of cultural awareness. We all develop at our own pace based on our experience; there is no right or wrong way to do so. Use the worksheet on the next page to examine your own progression through these stages.

Cultural Competency Journey Reflection

Where do I feel I am in my cultural-identity development?

_____

_____

_____

_____

What experiences have I had that have contributed to my current sense of self- and other-awareness?

_____

_____

_____

_____

Who have I encountered whose words or behaviors may be perceived by some as indicative of disrespect and disregard but that may instead be reflective of ethnocentric ignorance?

_____

_____

_____

_____

Diversity in Professional Training

I will now take a look at a research study that addresses variations in diversity training that exist within graduate mental health programs. Therapists have differing degrees of preparedness as it relates to multicultural awareness and competence. Many assume that they have had less personal experiences than other professionals around them and that others have received more training on the topic in their graduate programs. A team of researchers addressed this issue by surveying the various graduate programs that train aspiring therapists and found four different classifications of training programs (D'Andrea et al., 1991):

- **Culturally Entrenched**: A culturally entrenched training program rarely incorporates multicultural training. An example of this would be a 15-week counseling-related graduate course that assigns a large paper in the eighth week of class, which instructs students to answer questions related to the topic of the course, with the last question being "How do you think this topic relates to clients from various cultural backgrounds?" For the programs in this category, that's about as far as it goes.

- **Cross-Culturally Awakened**: A cross-culturally awakened training program has developed awareness of and engages in discussion of some cultural issues. Consider that same counseling graduate program, but instead of asking one diversity-related question in week eight, the entire lecture topic in the eighth week of class is devoted to applying that course's topic to clients of various cultural backgrounds. It is important to note here that the researchers found this classification to be the *most common type* of training program.

- **Cultural Integrity**: A training program in the cultural integrity stage gives increased attention to culture and provides separate courses on various issues related to culture. I have had the pleasure of teaching diversity-related courses in these graduate programs. Whether it's a broader course on diversity in counseling or a more specific themed course (e.g., gender and sexuality issues in counseling), these programs intentionally acknowledge varying mental health needs and recognize the potential influence of culture in the efforts to meet the needs of diverse cultural groups.

While more and more cultural-integrity courses are being created in light of a growing awareness that mental health professionals need increased multicultural preparedness, many undergraduate- and graduate-level diversity courses are still electives rather than required courses. As a result, students who choose to take these courses most often are those who already have an appreciation for cultural diversity or who expect to provide counseling services for a population that includes many ethnic minority individuals. We have yet to get to the point where every program includes multicultural awareness as a core requirement.

- **Infusion**: Finally, a training program in the infusion stage integrates multiculturalism into the whole curriculum. Unfortunately, many programs fear that in order to accomplish this, a complete overhaul of their program is necessary, including the display of various flags from around the world, the recreation of an entire curriculum, and even a change to the name of the training program to something like "The New Multicultural Marriage and Family Clinical Counseling Master's Degree Program." While some programs do indeed choose to make large changes like these, significant change can also occur through intentional efforts to address multicultural issues in every course. The goal is not to convey the message that "our program is unique because we also serve minorities" but to make efforts to become competent in meeting the needs of the greatest variety of clients possible.

As these classifications of training programs suggest, the unfortunate reality is that training programs in multicultural competence are often correlated with minimal efforts to adequately provide diversity training. That is to say that no matter how many good things your program offers—including renowned faculty, research-based curriculums, and accreditation—if your training program is not making intentional efforts to apply those services to serve the greatest variety of clients possible, then the program is limited in its scope of effectiveness. Training programs would benefit from acknowledging growth areas and limitations and prioritizing efforts to improve their cultural diversity training.

Limitations of Developmental Models

Before moving on from our discussion of competency development both at the individual level and in training programs, I think it is beneficial to acknowledge the limitations of developmental models on a topic such as cultural competency.

Overemphasis on Knowledge

One key limitation of developmental models is the assumption that cultural competency requires only the acquisition of knowledge. While I will address several factors that contribute to competence later, I can acknowledge here that it is more than knowledge and skills. Reading and learning about the history of a particular cultural group is definitely beneficial, as it provides opportunities to learn new things about people who have experiences other than your own. However, self-awareness, understanding, empathy, and rapport are more critical in developing relevant knowledge that has practical benefits.

Lack of Empirical Support

It is worth acknowledging that while empirically supported and evidenced-based practices tend to be the gold standard for developmental models on cultural competency, these models do not and cannot meet this standard. However, this does not invalidate their legitimacy. In many ways, it would be ethically inappropriate to meet that standard if doing so meant abruptly immersing people into another culture simply to study whether negative reactions might manifest as a result. In addition, theories based too heavily on specific terms and definitions are less relevant when those terms and definitions change across individuals, families, communities, geographic regions, and time. For some, the lack of empirical support for these models is a deal-breaker, but those willing to acknowledge the research despite its limitations can benefit from developing an increased understanding as a result of this research.

Limited Diversity in Research Participants

Another common challenge of many research studies is that they rarely obtain a culturally diverse demographic population of participants, resulting in research that is often disproportionately populated with college-age White males. These research studies often end the discussion of their results with a speculation as to what might be similar or different if the same study was attempted with individuals from a cultural minority background. Unfortunately, there are few academic professionals investing the time to answer those questions with new and diverse participants. So opportunities remain to improve our knowledge regarding the development of cultural competence by conducting updated research with diverse populations.

Limited Scope

Many diversity training programs focus exclusively on how therapists can improve interactions with their clients, unintentionally excluding interactions between supervisors and their supervisees, between professionals and their colleagues, and with the larger community in which their services are offered.

Consider the scenario where I was in a breakroom with a colleague while working at a large counseling agency. We were discussing a news story, and my colleague said something that was less culturally considerate than I thought was appropriate. When this colleague saw my subtle, nonverbal reaction to the comment, the colleague offered a reassuring, "Oh, don't worry, I would never say that kind of thing in front of a client." What this colleague didn't consider was that if it was inappropriate for a therapist-client interaction, then it may also have been inappropriate for a therapist-colleague relationship, or any relationship for that matter. Unfortunately, this broader scope of "application across varying relationships" is not often taught as a part of most diversity training. In order to truly be effective, diversity training needs to be applied to all aspects of personal and professional interaction and service.

Limited Awareness

Ignorance and unintentional offenses can negatively impact our interactions with our clients, whether or not we are consciously aware of them. Therefore, if we are unaware of our impact on others, we will understandably lack sufficient motivation to solve these problems when they arise. In light of this, diversity training programs must provide strategies that help professionals make the most of every opportunity to reduce their ignorance and increase their knowledge and understanding, so they can make better decisions in consideration of their needs and abilities, as well as the needs and experiences of others.

Limited Confidence

Professionals tasked with training existing and aspiring professionals on the topic of multicultural awareness and diversity often feel intimidated by their own undesirable and seemingly unacceptable level of ignorance. Many feel that they themselves are insufficiently trained. Many avoid any topic or experience that seems scary or uncomfortable, resulting in their feeling intimidated by ignorance. For example, a therapist may conclude that since his clients know more about their own cultural experiences, it is best for him to not risk saying anything about these cultural experiences for fear that he will offend them.

While I appreciate that we should aspire to avoid overconfidence and to avoid assuming that we know so much, we should also not minimize the knowledge we do have. Yes, our clients should always be considered the experts on their own lives and cultural experiences. And although there is a time for learning about our clients from our clients, there is also a time for using the knowledge we do have to enhance our clients' understanding of their own cultural experiences. If done well, we can maintain appropriate confidence in what we know and just as confidently acknowledge what we don't know, while being both flexible and respectful throughout the process.

Limited Experiences

As mentioned previously, effective cultural competence includes a combination of academic knowledge and personal experiences. Therefore, diversity training programs would benefit from including research that has been informed by real-life experiences and from also including opportunities for practical application of the theories and concepts provided by the academic research. Not only is this what makes the academic efforts worth the investment, but the consequent practical experience would hopefully inform more effective research in an endless learning and experiential loop that improves real-life relationship interactions in our communities.

Common Diverse-Staff Myth

Finally, there is a common myth that the recruitment of diverse staff automatically results in a functioning multicultural program. While this may seem to be a reasonable solution to a problem, it is not always as easy as it may seem.

THE BOARD ROOM

Consider... a meeting of the partners at a successful law firm in a large metropolitan city. These partners make up a stereotypical homogeneous group: older, White, male, and of high socioeconomic status. Needless to say, they have a lot in common. But the leader of the meeting acknowledges this trend and tells the group that they are not doing as well as they should be when it comes to offering services and meeting the needs of the diverse population in the community surrounding their building. To remedy this problem, they conclude that they need to be more diverse.

At the next quarterly meeting of partners, the leader introduces everyone to their newest partner—a young, African American male. The leader expresses a desire to pick up where they left off at the previous meeting, with the hopes of brainstorming ways to reach diverse populations in the community. It is then that the new partner realizes that all eyes in the room have turned to him and unofficially given him the floor to share his thoughts. The new partner shares that while he is grateful for the opportunity to contribute, he will sadly have to disappoint them because he doesn't feel he has much to share on the topic. When asked why, he explains that while the hue of his skin may be different than that of others in the room, he also grew up in the suburbs in a high socioeconomic household, received a Harvard education, and has very few significant experiences with the diverse communities the firm is seeking to better understand.

What went wrong? Although the partners did not have negative intentions, they assumed if they were just able to change the composition of the group, then it would result in a functioning multicultural organization. It was a reasonable assumption. Odds are that if you find someone who looks different, they have likely have had different experiences than you have. However, this is not always the case. Therefore, individuals and organizations would benefit from welcoming leaders who have different perspectives and experiences to offer and from making a commitment to multicultural issues and creating a positive work environment to nurture them.

THE CAMPUS PHOTO

Consider... a Latino college student at a large university who is greeted at his dorm room by his excited roommate, who informs him that the course catalog has been released and that he is included in the campus photo used for the cover. This student finds that revelation interesting because he doesn't remember posing for any photo or being notified that he would be included on the cover. Upon close inspection of the cover, the student realizes that he has been photoshopped into the photo, along with a few other students of ethnic backgrounds. While the university made an effort to ensure that the diversity in the photo was representative of the proportion of ethnic minority students who actually attend the university, the fact that they had to manufacture the photo leaves many feeling disturbed. After this incident, the university creates an office of diversity, equity, and inclusion with the explicit intention of reducing offenses like these and increasing the quality of experiences for students from diverse cultural backgrounds.

What went wrong here? Was it wrong to try to convey to prospective students the cultural diversity that exists on campus? I think not. After all, the ethnic diversity represented in the photo represented approximately the percentage of ethnic diversity of the student population. However, the problem rests in the reality that the photo was deceptively manufactured.

Whatever your role may be in your organization, make the most of opportunities to help create a genuine environment that welcomes and supports diverse experiences and contributions. This will benefit the organization and its staff, and it will create an environment conducive to all people.

On the next few pages, you will find a worksheet to help you examine your experience of cultural competency within your professional organization, as well as a self-assessment tool to examine how you can attract, welcome, encourage, and protect staff and clients from various cultural backgrounds.

Cultural Competency Journey Reflection

In what ways have I, or an organization I have been a part of, unintentionally perpetuated the diverse-staff myth?

_____

_____

_____

_____

How can I help create an environment where diverse experiences and backgrounds can be appreciated?

_____

_____

_____

_____

How can I intentionally include diverse perspectives in my professional efforts to meet a greater variety of needs?

_____

_____

_____

_____

Multicultural Awareness in the Workplace

While the development of multicultural awareness and competence on an individual level can definitely impact and improve any professional environment, efforts can also be made on a business- or organization-wide level to more effectively meet the needs of staff and clients from a greater variety of cultural backgrounds.

Take a moment to explore the efforts that can be taken in your current professional setting to **attract**, **welcome**, **encourage**, and **protect** staff and clients from various cultural backgrounds.

Attract

Advertising: In what ways do we intentionally advertise to and show that we desire to meet the needs of potential clients from various cultural backgrounds (e.g., showing appreciation for various cultures; considering the languages and photos chosen for websites, brochures, flyers, and other advertisements; offering services specific to the needs of the community at affordable prices and accessible locations)?

_____

_____

_____

_____

Hiring: What efforts do we make to intentionally avoid microaggressions and discrimination during the interview process? In what ways do we seek to hire individuals with varying perspectives and life experiences?

_____

_____

_____

_____

Welcome

Valuing: In what ways do we make accommodations to make everyone feel comfortable and a valuable contributor to the group (e.g., installation of wheelchair ramps, family medical leave for parents, various foods offerings in the cafeteria, time off for an expanded list of religious holidays)?

_____

_____

_____

_____

Encourage

Sustaining: In what ways do we intentionally assess and reassess how we are doing in our efforts to meet a greater variety of diverse needs (e.g., meeting with employees and community leaders, requesting and encouraging feedback on our progress in meeting their needs)?

_____

_____

_____

Protect

Preventing: In what ways is it clear that discrimination and harassment are not tolerated and that there are clear and enforceable policies for staff who do not comply with this standard (e.g., being willing to fire someone who is pervasively oppressive, initiating reconciliation and conflict resolution prior to firing for the benefit of everyone involved)?

_____

_____

_____

Responding: In what ways do we encourage, receive, and effectively respond to reports of discrimination and harassment in our work environment (e.g., if you see something, say something, and we will address the concern expressed)?

_____

_____

_____

What Is Multicultural Diversity?

Before we get too far into our exploration of a practical perspective of multicultural diversity, let's make sure we're talking about the same thing when we use the phrase. Multicultural diversity includes several factors, such as:

Culture	Gender	Socioeconomic status
Race	Sexual orientation	Geographic region
Ethnicity	Ability	Politics
Age	Religion	...and more

When we talk about diversity, it includes more than just race and ethnicity. Diverse simply means different, and there are many ways in which we are similar to and different from those with whom we interact.

THE BOARD ROOM—REVISITED

Let's revisit the meeting of partners at the law firm. In the conversation prior to their decision to hire a new lawyer, the leader suggested that they consider hiring someone to help enhance their perspective and diversify the team. Someone toward the middle of the conference room raised their hand and asked, "So we should hire a woman—since we're all men here—and that would offer an opportunity for a different perspective?" A little caught off guard, the leader responded, "Well, actually, that's not what I had in mind." The interjector then suggested, "Oh, then you want to hire someone who identifies as gay or lesbian since none of us here have expressed any knowledge or experience in reaching out to those who identify as a part of the LGBTQ+ community?" The leader was again caught off guard, not knowing how to respond.

What was happening here? The leader had one particular idea in mind when he thought of being more "diverse"—namely, it was synonymous with an ethnic minority. However, as the additional clarification questions illustrate, there are various ways that we can be more diverse. Maybe you can include someone who expresses different religious or political beliefs. Maybe you can include someone who has experience meeting the needs of those living in a different part of the state or country, and that different perspective may be just what your organization needs to spark creativity and enhance the services currently being provided. Therefore, when you refer to diversity, be intentional and specific about what type of diversity you are referring to. And if someone around you speaks of diversity, maybe you will be able to find a polite and respectful way to encourage them to be more specific in their meaning as well.

Majority and Minority Culture

In the United States, we have a tendency to use certain default words to describe categories of people. The idea here being that since the majority of the American population identifies as White Non-Hispanic, and the remaining minority of the population identifies as one of the many varieties of persons of color, then it should be safe and descriptive to use nonspecific terms, such as *majority culture* and *minority culture*, to describe different people. The thought here is that by avoiding more specific terms, we avoid the risk that we will offend someone by using an undesirable term. While there is merit to this strategy, we must acknowledge that it has its limits. Specifically, as population demographics have changed, these terms don't necessarily hold the easily recognizable meaning they once held.

According to a report by the U.S. Census Bureau, based on trends in birth, death, and immigration rates, it is projected that by the year 2044, ethnic minority groups will collectively exceed 51 percent of the United States population (Colby & Ortman, 2015). Therefore, there could be a day when someone referring to individuals in the minority culture could be referring to those who identify as White Americans. Now, sharing this statistical projection is not intended to have any positive or negative implications. It is simply to challenge you to be intentional with the terms of reference you choose, to acknowledge the limitations of those references, and to supportively encourage those around you to do the same.

White Is Also a Color in the Crayon Box

A common myth is that individuals who identify as White Americans don't have culture. Many White people express that they don't feel like they have a strong cultural heritage that significantly influences their daily lives (e.g., with unique holidays and events, culture-specific foods, clothing styles, music). Some go so far as to feel jealous of those who do identify with a strong cultural tradition—not because they wish they had those specific cultural traditions but because they wish they had some of their own.

When helping professionals express concerns like these—often as a justification for why they don't feel like they have a right to discuss culture-related issues with their clients, or why they have difficulty understanding and relating to individuals who have a stronger cultural identification than themselves—my response is usually "White is a color in the crayon box too." After all, many of these same individuals have no difficulty identifying with their cultural background on occasions such as St. Patrick's Day (e.g., with "Kiss Me I'm Irish" paraphernalia) and when interacting with others in culture-emphasized areas, such as New York's Little Italy. This is not a sign of hypocrisy but an indication of a need to recognize that while we may or may not identify with our cultural background as much as someone else may identify with theirs, that doesn't mean we don't have a cultural background with which to identify.

The growing popularity of genetic testing technology has mildly decreased this tendency, as people are utilizing these programs to find out who they are and where they come from. While DNA can tell us where we came from genetically, we all have individual choice regarding which aspects of our cultural heritage we choose to embrace. As helping professionals, we are best served when we take the time to personally and professionally wrestle with and increase our own cultural self-awareness so we are better prepared to help our clients wrestle with their cultural self-awareness.

Changing Population

As we increase our understanding of what diversity includes, we improve our ability to see how many of the differences between those we consider like us and those we consider different from us change over location and time. Many people struggle with adjusting to changes in their environment and thus their view of the world. In order to help others adjust to the changes in their families and communities, let's review some of the many ways in which population demographics have changed, as well as some of the benefits of helping people adjust well to those changes.

Ethnicity

In our effort to increase our awareness of ourselves and others, it is a good idea to consider who we are as it also relates to who makes up the country in which we live.

According to the U.S. Census Bureau, ethnic diversity in America can be approximately reflected as follows (Colby & Ortman, 2015):

- 79 percent White
- 17 percent Hispanic
- 14 percent Black
- 6 percent Asian
- 2 percent American Indian/Alaska Native
- 1 percent Native Hawaiian/Other Pacific Islander
- 3 percent mixed

For many individuals, these statistical proportions reflect the real-life experiences they encounter every day in their community. However, many others have vastly different personal experiences. These demographic differences are significant because it is natural for us to feel more competent and confident when we're working with certain populations with which we are most familiar. It naturally produces a professional comfort zone that certainly has its professional benefits. However, as population demographics change, helping professionals must learn to adapt by expanding their understanding of the world outside of their comfort zone in order to remain relevant and effective. Even if you're able to live and work in your comfort zone, those you serve may not live in the same world and may need help applying and adapting what they learn from you to the larger world.

Age

In addition to ethnic population changes, there are also relevant age-related changes that are worth acknowledging. According to the U.S. Census Bureau, approximately 15 percent of the population is 65 years old or older—and that percentage is growing (He et al., 2016). Practically speaking, people are living longer. Helping professionals thus need to be aware of the similarities and differences of the experiences of individuals across various stages of the life span. What is important to us when we are younger may not hold the same significance as we age. What we struggle with or worry about may also change as we age.

Professionally, those who don't specialize in serving older adults will eventually have less of a luxury to assert that they "just don't work with that population." Instead, helping professionals need to be sure that they are not indirectly and unintentionally minimizing the value and beliefs of older adults. I encourage you to embrace and cultivate your area of specialty, whatever it may be, but to also make efforts not to let your personal and professional preference turn into a belief system that devalues or minimizes the experiences of those not within your specialty. The goal is to be progressively more equipped to meet the needs of whoever seeks your assistance.

Gender and Sexuality

According to a Gallup Poll (Jones, 2021), approximately 5.6 percent of American adults identify themselves somewhere in the LGBTQ+ community. While many therapists conclude that this aspect of cultural diversity does not apply to them since they do not specialize in working with the LGBTQ+ population, statistically speaking, 5.6 percent of the clients they serve may identify as such. The key word in that statistic is *identify*. Despite the societal changes in acceptance and the legalization of same-sex marriage, there are many who do not accept individuals who identify as something other than heterosexual and cisgender. Things may be legal in the country but may not feel so legal in someone's home, church, or community. Regardless of our differing beliefs and values, we need to do our best as helping professionals to let our clients know we can offer support.

Expanding the Definition of Diversity

In the following figure, you will see diverse cultural dimensions reflected in the diversity wheel created by the Diversity Leadership Council at Johns Hopkins University (2020). In their effort to visually represent a broad scope of diversity, they proposed that some cultural expressions are permanent or visible, such as race or ethnicity and gender, while others are acquired and change over the course of a lifetime, such as family role and income.

The combinations of all of these dimensions influence our values, beliefs, behaviors, experiences, and expectations and make us all unique as individuals. The diversity wheel reminds us to consider more than just race and ethnicity when examining the role diversity plays in our efforts as helping professionals. These diverse factors include age, gender, national origin, sexual orientation, mental/physical ability, and race/ethnicity, as well as broader factors, such as:

- Work experience (e.g., white-collar job, blue-collar job)
- Education (e.g., doctoral degree, bachelor's degree, diploma, GED)
- Political belief (e.g., Republican, Democrat, Independent)
- Family role (e.g., mother, father, sister, brother, cousin)
- Organizational role (e.g., company president, executive assistant, custodial engineer)
- Communication and language skills (e.g., English as a first language, second language, American Sign Language, Braille)
- Income (e.g., high, middle, or low socioeconomic status)
- Religion (e.g., Christian, Muslim, Buddhist)
- Appearance (e.g., height, build, shape)

Some people admittedly have aversions to conceptualizations such as these because it doesn't acknowledge an aspect of their identity that is very important to them (e.g., geographic region, special talents, values, or special interests). However, the benefit of the diversity wheel is not in its exhaustiveness but in its support in considering a broad scope of understanding in how we are all diverse.

Similarly, some people have aversions to the diversity wheel because it can be used to limit people by the labels with which they identify. However, despite the admittedly negative experiences many have endured due to misused descriptors, the emphasis need not be on the limits of labels as much as their practical use in identifying ways in which we are all similar to and different from others.

For example, consider a scenario in which you meet someone for the first time and that person, interested in getting to know you better, asks you to tell them three things about yourself. What would you say? What descriptors would come to mind? Personally, my answer might begin with "Well, I'm an African American, Christian, male..." Already, I have begun to use labels to identify factors about myself that also describe ways in which I may be similar to and different from others. By identifying myself as African American, I have utilized one of the inner dimensions on the diversity wheel: race/ethnicity. By identifying myself as Christian, I have utilized the outer dimension category of religion. And by identifying myself as male, I have utilized the inner dimension category of gender.

Now, if given enough time, I could identify where I feel I fit in each of the categories listed. Since the diversity wheel is not exhaustive, I could also identify other categories and descriptors that are relevant to who I am. Despite the non-exhaustive limitations of this conceptualization, it can still serve as a visual reminder that there are various ways we can be similar to or different from almost anyone we encounter.

TWO COWORKERS GO TO THE FAIR

Consider... two coworkers who visit a health and wellness fair where the booths are categorized by the population for whom they are targeting their services—and they are using the categories on the diversity wheel as their guide. Since the coworkers' friendship is based on their being so alike, they decide to explore the fair together. When they visit the Organizational Role section of the fair, they walk toward the table that contains information and services for executive assistants. Then they visit the Socioeconomic section, where they visit a table that offers information to those whose income is in the range they share.

Next, they approach the Political Beliefs section, but upon entering, one coworker walks toward the table offering information for Democrats, while the other walks toward the table offering information for Republicans. The coworkers stop and look at each other, confused. One says to the other, "What are you doing? Why are you over there? I thought we were walking around the fair together. I thought we were the same." The other coworker responds, "We are the same in many ways. But in this way, we're different."

And it is at this point where their friendship has the potential to be tested. In order for their relationship to survive and thrive, they need to accept the reality that they can be similar in a lot of ways but can also differ in other ways. Additionally, they would benefit even more from going beyond accepting those differences. In particular, it would serve them well to learn more about these differences and the ways these differences can enhance their relationship rather than being an inconvenience.

The ways we identify ourselves can change over time, both at a group and individual level. We would benefit from remembering that diversity includes more than just race and ethnicity and from recognizing that no matter how much we have in common with someone, we also have our differences. And no matter how different someone may seem to you, you likely have something in common with them as well. Increased cultural competence involves improving your awareness of these similarities and differences and valuing the role each can play in strengthening your personal and professional relationships.

Cultural Genograms

Genograms are one of the most basic assessment tools used by mental health professionals to gain a better understanding of extended family dynamics. In practical reality, genograms are family trees on steroids. You begin by taking a family tree, with its circles and squares, connected by genealogical lines, and then you enhance it with various symbols representing relationship dynamics between family members (e.g., divorce, separation, adoption, and close, as well as cut-off, relationships).

Another key benefit of genograms is that as you learn more about the individual you are trying to help, the genogram can reveal family patterns that may not have been evident and that may be influencing current progress or struggles. For example, when working with someone who is struggling with substance abuse, it may be significant to know that there is a history of substance abuse in their immediate and extended family. Or when working with someone who is having marital difficulties and considering divorce, it may be significant to know that they have a family history of divorces within the first five years of marriage.

Cultural genograms are enhanced genograms in that the structure is the same and the exploration of potentially relevant patterns is also the same (Hardy & Laszloffy, 1995). However, cultural genograms intentionally look for a greater variety of potentially significant factors and patterns. Some of these factors include:

- Gender
- Age
- Build
- Skin and hair
- Facial features

- Other physical features
- Nationality/ethnicity
- Cultural background
- Family economic resources

- Religious orientation
- Educational background
- Physical and health abilities
- Sexual orientation

The expectation is not to explore each and every one of these factors for every possible family member. Rather, it is to consider and listen for the potential relevance of these culturally significant factors (and if signs and patterns arise, to further explore them).

THE SIBLINGS

Consider... a therapist who is creating a genogram with a client, gathering basic information such as family members' names, ages, and relationship dynamics. The therapist then realizes that each of the client's four siblings have partners or spouses whose names suggest they are from a different ethnic background. Upon further exploration, the therapist learned that the client's mother divorced her husband when the client was a child and remarried someone from another ethnic background. As the children grew older, they dated individuals from various cultural backgrounds, but when it came time to get married and choose a life partner, they chose spouses from the same cultural background as their mother's spouse. The client states that she (and, to her knowledge, her siblings as well) didn't make a conscious decision to do so; that's just how it worked out. However, she later adds that there may have been a subconscious belief that "if it's good enough for Mom, then that's good enough for me."

Several months later, this same therapist meets another client who is also from a divorced household and who also happens to be one of four siblings. During an information-gathering genogram activity, the therapist notices a similar trend where the siblings' partners or spouses have names suggesting they are from a different ethnic background. The therapist speculates that the new stepfather provided the siblings with similar motivation to the previous case, only to find out that the mother never remarried or had any significant intimate relationships after her divorce.

Confused, the therapist explores the case further and learns that after the divorce, the mother relocated with her children to a geographic region where the demographics were significantly different—more specifically, the ethnic group in which the family was accustomed to being in the majority was now in the minority. As a result, this provided the children with potential dating partners from one particular ethnic group more so than others.

Although the end result looked very similar between these two families, the factors that contributed to these outcomes were different. Cultural genograms have the potential to reveal a lot about a person's motivations and behaviors, whether they are aware of them or not. In addition, the cultural genogram serves as a good reminder to consider the various possible contributing factors to the trends and behaviors that we see on a daily basis.

Cultural Self-Assessment

In an effort to increase your understanding of the significance of cultural experiences and values on others, it is beneficial to increase your own cultural self-awareness as well. Investing time in exploring your own identity, values, and beliefs helps you broaden your perspective on the various ways in which these factors can influence your life and can help you empathize more effectively with others as they embark upon their own self-discovery journeys.

To assist you in beginning this personal self-awareness journey, I recommend asking yourself the following questions and contemplating the implications of your answers on your personal cultural identity, values, and beliefs, as well as the impact on your personal and professional interactions:

> **What aspects of your cultural identity
> do you value or identify with most? Why?**

How would you respond if someone were to ask, "Who are you? Tell me something about yourself." Using the diversity wheel as a guide, consider various labels you would use to identify yourself: groups you are a part of, values and beliefs you hold, or roles you play in your daily life. Now, of those considerations, what are the first three that come to mind? Once you have the answer to that question, ask yourself a follow-up question by exploring *why* you chose those answers.

It is worth noting that some of the descriptors we use to identify ourselves represent the roles we play in our lives. These roles have clear titles and meanings, and they also have a beginning and an end point. For example, before the birth of my daughters, being a father was not one of the ways I would have identified myself. Now, though, not only is it on my list, but it is also one of the most important ways I see myself.

Many people believe that diversity is something others have to deal with, but that's only because they surround themselves with similar people. This the same trap that the two coworkers found themselves in: believing that just because they had some things in common that they had all things in common. Even if you listed out the ways you identify yourself across a variety of categories—and even if a small percentage of the population shared exactly the same answers as you—only a smaller percentage of that already small percentage would continue to share your answers to the question of *why* you identify that way. The odds are good that while you may share similar traits, characteristics, and values as many other people, there will likely be large or very subtle differences between you and those whom you consider to be like you. **Therefore, we all need to learn to accept our own identity while also accepting other people for who they are, no matter how similar or different they may be**.

In addition to examining our identity, it is beneficial to explore and acknowledge *how* our beliefs and values came to be. One of the most common difficulties people have when it comes to empathizing with and accepting others' beliefs is the conclusion that their own beliefs are correct or best. Some people end up forming such strongly held beliefs because they have considered and weighed multiple options (and have settled on what they believe to be the most founded and beneficial). But other people go on to develop such strong beliefs because that is what was taught or modeled to them growing up. To help discern how you formed your value and belief system, explore the lessons and examples you received from your family of origin and from other early learning experiences:

> **What messages did you receive (directly or indirectly)**
> **about your family's cultural identity growing up?**

For many, this challenge is easy, as they can identify several overt messages conveyed to them by their parents and loved ones. For example, some were taught that they had certain character traits because of their ethnic background (e.g., "We come from a long line of Germans.") Others were expected to pursue certain life goals because doing so was central to their family name and family reputation (e.g., "Your great-grandmother was a teacher, your grandmother was a teacher, I am a teacher, and one day I look forward to seeing you teach the next generation.")

Others received messages that may have been just as strong but indirect. For example, someone may have had a family history of divorce and seen unhealthy relationships modeled. In turn, they may lack relationships skills as an adult and have no context for healthy relationships. In cases like these, it is understandable that someone could learn to have a very poor value for marriage, not pursue marriage themselves, and even encourage others to avoid marriage. They are sincerely trying to avoid and protect others from the unhealthy experiences they have had or have seen modeled for them in the past. Indirect messages can still play a significant role in the words and actions conveyed in our everyday lives.

Our beliefs, our values, and how we see ourselves in relation to others naturally impact how we interact with others. Therefore, as we increase our ownership of our identity, it is beneficial to explore the ways our self-identity enhances our ability to understand and support others, as well as the ways it hinders healthy personal and professional relationships:

> ## How does your cultural identity influence your view of the world and the people in it (positively or negatively)?

While it is certainly beneficial to explore the direct and indirect lessons we have learned that influence our everyday lives, it is also critical that we acknowledge the potential impact of our personal beliefs and values on our clients, including how the manner in which we see ourselves in relation to the world affects our efforts to understand, empathize with, and effectively support our clients. At the end of the day, our self-awareness is relevant to the degree to which it enhances or hinders our ability to help others understand themselves:

> ## How does your cultural identity influence your view of your clients?

The goal of these efforts at increasing self-awareness is to identify as many influencing factors on who we are today and to make intentional efforts to reduce any unintentional harm and increase the positive impact we have on others. Use the worksheet on the next page to fill in your answers for these multicultural self-awareness questions.

Increasing Multicultural Self-Awareness

Multicultural awareness and diversity include more than your ethnic background. They also include:

- Age
- Race/ethnicity
- National origin
- Gender

- Family role
- Sexual orientation
- Mental/physical ability
- Income

- Religion
- Education
- Communication & language skills
- Appearance

- Political beliefs
- Work experience
- Organizational role

In order to more effectively help others explore and understand the significance of their cultural identity on their life, take a moment to explore the various aspects of your own cultural identity.

What aspects of my cultural identity do I identify with or value most?

_____

_____

_____

_____

Why do I identify with or value these aspects of my identity?

_____

_____

_____

_____

What messages did I receive (directly or indirectly) about my or my family's cultural identity growing up?

_____

_____

_____

_____

How does this influence my view of the world and the people in it (positively or negatively)?

_____

_____

_____

_____

How does this influence my view of my clients?

_____

_____

_____

_____

Commonly Misunderstood Vocabulary

In professional and casual conversations with others, it is common for certain words to have such strong associations that the words take on extra meaning—often negatively so. You may find that the following words are examples of this in your life. Consequently, miscommunication ensues when people interpret these words differently and the potential for relationship damage increases. I believe that while language is flexible in many ways, it is beneficial to acknowledge the depth, as well as the limitations, of the words we use. This is especially pertinent on the topic of multicultural awareness and diversity, when people are already overly cautious and uncertain of people's intentions.

With that in mind, let's explore some common words related to multicultural awareness and diversity and identify some guiding principles for understanding and using these words in conversations that promote healthy relationship interactions.

> **Bias:**
> A particular tendency or inclination about something, especially one associated with prejudice or partiality. **Conscious bias** (also known as **explicit bias**) and **unconscious bias** (also known as **implicit bias**) differ in the degree to which a person is aware of their bias.

The word *bias* often has an negative connotation, which has the effect of turning people off to whomever the word is applied. For example, you might hear someone say, "Hey, can you believe Sally? She is so biased." However, if we consider the most basic definition of the word, we don't necessarily have to assume a negative connotation. If I have a piece of candy, and there are two children between whom I have the choice to give that piece of candy and one of them is my child, then I will admit that I am biased toward my daughter. I have a particular inclination toward her, and most importantly, I don't feel ashamed about it.

Now if my bias leads me to always give things to my daughter at the exclusion of others, if I convince myself that my daughter is more deserving of candy (and that others are less deserving), or if I convince myself that other kids don't even like candy, then that bias becomes problematic. You don't have to judge others or yourself for having inclinations and leanings. The question you should ask is whether that leaning contributes to a lack of consideration and mistreatment of some in favor of others.

That is where the problem with bias arises in practical daily use. So acknowledge and admit your biases without shame or judgment. Then take responsibility for reducing any negative or unfair treatment of others that may result from them.

> **Prejudice:**
> Any preconceived opinion or feeling,
> either favorable or unfavorable

It is a very common reality that saying or hearing the word *prejudice* automatically generates uncomfortable and often negative feelings, even if it's not associated with a specific person. Therefore, it is often difficult to explore the word neutrally. For the purposes of this conversation, let's break down the word into its components: to pre-judge. Some people, in their efforts to avoid any type of prejudice in themselves, look for and shame any sign of pre-judgments in others (e.g., "How do you dare to have any pre-judgements about someone else without first giving them an opportunity to tell us who they are!") This is often echoed by the adage that "you can't judge a book by its cover."

While this is generally a good rule to live by, in its extreme form, it is not always accurate. After all, sometimes you can pre-judge. If I hand you a book with Batman on the cover, and you open the book and begin to read, "In the beginning God created the heavens and the earth…," how many pages do you think it would take before you would stop and ask, "Where is Batman in this story?" Likely not long, because there is often a reasonable expectation that what is on the cover should give you at least a good first impression about what to expect from the inside of the book; and when it doesn't, confusion is reasonable.

In our interactions with real people, it is similarly reasonable to have thoughts and judgments—as well as assumptions and conclusions—from the first encounters we have with others. That's not a bad thing in and of itself. We have to make certain assumptions to live and interact in this world. The problem arises when we allow our pre-judgments to dictate our interactions with others regardless of the words and actions that follow those first impressions. When we paste our pre-judgments onto others and convey (directly or indirectly) that it doesn't matter what they say or do— when we express that our minds have been made up, that we know everything we need to know, and that nothing they say or do will change that—this results in negative outcomes for others. We see this a lot when individuals are in authority roles where their pre-judgments can negatively influence decisions for those working under them. That's where pre-judgments understandably gain the negative association attributed to prejudice.

Instead of overcompensating and judging ourselves and others for having any pre-judgments, we would be better served to increase our awareness of them, to correct any unwarranted initial thoughts, to give people opportunities to show us who they are, and to then go the extra step of treating people the way their actions warrant, rather than based on our preconceptions.

> **Stereotype:**
> A widely held, but fixed and oversimplified, image or idea
> of a particular type of person or thing

Similar to pre-judgments, stereotypes can impact relationships when we let our personally fixed ideas of things and people impact how we treat them, more so than what their words and actions recommend. Some people falsely conclude that as long as a stereotype is a positive one, that there can be no negative consequences to that stereotype. Unfortunately, even positive stereotypes can have a negative impact. For example, many tall individuals are shamed for not fitting into the stereotype that tall people are naturally athletic. There are also many Asian Americans who are shamed for not fitting into the stereotype that all Asian Americans should know martial arts or be naturally gifted mathematicians.

Stereotypes are based on a lot of things and often are the result of past experiences. Stereotypes are intended to help us learn from past experiences and thereby avoid similar unpleasant experiences in the future. While having preconceived ideas is not always a bad thing, it is what we do with these stereotypes that influences their impact.

Our challenge as helping professionals is not to try to avoid all stereotypes or to shame ourselves and others for any that we discover. Rather, increase your self-awareness of stereotypes as they arise, explore the experiences that contributed to them, test their validity, and be willing to modify stereotypes and interact with others based on who they let you know that they are, rather than who you conclude they should be based on your stereotypes.

> **Discrimination:**
> Treatment in favor of or against someone based on the
> category that person belongs to rather than on individual merit

Since the word *discriminate* also has a negative association, let's consider its root word: to discern. In every service we provide, we have to discern what we will do, how much we can do, where we will do it, and so on. However, there are times when some people feel left out and conclude that there was an intentional effort to exclude them.

THE CLINIC

Consider... a director of a mental health clinic who was accused of discrimination. A prospective client expressed feeling excluded because the brochure and clinic documentation were not in the language in which she and her family were fluent. This director felt conflicted because the clinic's leadership made intentional efforts to offer as many services as possible to meet the greatest variety of client needs as they were able. At the same time, this clinic was not in an area where there was a large population of individuals and families who spoke that particular language.

In exploring the issue with the clinic's leadership, the conclusion was drawn that the lack of documentation in multiple languages was not indicative of discrimination as much as it was a strategic planning choice in consideration of limited resources and the cultural makeup of the surrounding community. The clinic even committed to being willing to change their strategic plan if the population and needs of the community significantly changed. After having conducted this honest evaluation of the accusation of discrimination, the director proposed a compromise to the woman who felt excluded by agreeing to provide an interpreter to assist with language interpretation.

In your helping efforts, you may find yourself seeing signs of potential discrimination or being accused of discrimination. The goal in these circumstances is not to let the perception or accusation be the end of the conversation. Rather, be willing to critically explore the motives behind, as well as the outcomes of, your actions. You may discover that though your intentions may have been sincere, there were people left out whose needs you were in the best position to meet.

In these cases, change is appropriate, but the accusation of discrimination need not characterize you or your organization. Rather, you can provide an empathetic response, such as "Thank you for letting me know of your concern. We were not aware that our intentions were not as effective as we had hoped. But now that we know, we will make efforts to remedy that oversight for the benefit of you and others who have not been effectively served." When you thank others for bringing the issue to your attention, it validates their feelings and gives them hope that change is likely in the future. It has the potential to reduce some of the intensity of the accusation and the impact of the felt exclusion. It also affirms the belief that sharing concerns will bring about change.

In your professional life, I encourage you to make intentional efforts to explore whose needs are being met and whose needs you can also most effectively meet. You can't do everything for everyone all of the time. If you discover that you have a tendency to meet some needs at the exclusion of others, based on factors other than available resources or merit, then be willing to take responsibility for the need to improve.

Oppression:
The exercise of authority or power in an unjust manner
(physically or emotionally)

Unlike the other words mentioned in this section, I can offer no neutral understanding of the word *oppression*. By definition, it involves unjust emotional or physical misuse of one's ability to influence another person. I have included it in the discussion because it often has the same or similar automatic negative associations as the other terms discussed. Hopefully by now it is more evident that these words are not all synonymous.

Use the worksheet on the next page to examine how bias, prejudice, stereotypes, discrimination, and oppression may impact your actions or beliefs.

Cultural Self-Assessment

Multicultural Impact Awareness

Some words tend to have such strong negative associations that we are uncomfortable exploring the potential appropriateness of those words as descriptors of our actions or beliefs. However, if we take a look at the core principles being conveyed by these words, we may be willing to consider the reasonable ways that they may apply to our lives. As a result, we may be better prepared to make beneficial changes for personal and relational improvement.

Take a look at the following words, and explore the ways they might describe your actions or beliefs. Then explore ways that you can improve your interactions with others as a result of your increased self-awareness.

> **Bias:** A particular tendency or inclination about something, especially one associated with prejudice or partiality

What biases might I have (and how might they be influencing my interactions with my clients)? How might I show more balance where appropriate?

_____

_____

_____

> **Prejudice:** Any preconceived opinion or feeling, either favorable or unfavorable

What preconceived opinions do I have for certain clients that influence how I interact with them before our initial interaction? How might I test or reduce the negative impact of those preconceived thoughts?

_____

_____

_____

> **Stereotype:** A widely held, but fixed and oversimplified, image or idea of a particular type of person or thing

What oversimplified beliefs (positive or negative) do I have about people who are similar to or different from me? How might I test or reduce the negative impact of those beliefs?

_____

_____

_____

> **Discrimination:** Treatment in favor of or against someone based on the category a person belongs to rather than on individual merit

In what ways might I be unintentionally showing favor toward some clients while leaving out other clients? How might I show more balance where appropriate?

_____

_____

_____

> **Oppression:** The exercise of authority or power in an unjust manner (physically or emotionally)

In what ways might I be using power, influence, or privilege in my favor at the expense of someone else who might not have the same opportunities? How might I use any power, influence, or privilege I have to help someone who does not have the same opportunities?

_____

_____

_____

More **Commonly Misunderstood Vocabulary**

The collection of words previously discussed were similar to one another in their practical use, as well as in their frequent misunderstanding and misuse. The following words are similarly used in comparison to one another and are also frequently misunderstood and misused.

Diversity:
Difference; variety; dissimilarity

The word *diversity* is often used synonymously with the phrase *ethnic minority*. However, in its most basic form, diversity refers to the state of being different. As the diversity wheel conveyed, there are many ways we can be different from someone else. Therefore, the next time you hear someone suggest that an organization or group become more diverse, maybe you can be the one to respectfully ask, "How so? In what way did you have in mind to be more diverse?"

Minority:
A relatively smaller number,
especially compared to a larger group

Similar to diversity, the word *minority* is often used synonymously with ethnic minority. However, a person's status as a minority is, in part, dependent on their environment. For example, consider a female high school student who identifies as a middle-class White American and who lives in a predominately middle-class White neighborhood—but who attends a large high school whose student body is over 90 percent African American. While that student may be in the majority in the community outside of school, she is in a minority at school.

In some ways, that student knows how it feels to be a in minority in ways that her classmates do not because many of her classmates have never personally traveled beyond a 10-mile radius of their home, school, church, or grocery store. And although her peers distantly acknowledge their ethnic minority status, their daily interactions do not require them to acknowledge it on a daily basis. Therefore, the next time you hear someone suggest that an organization or group reach out to more minorities, maybe you can be the one to respectfully ask, "How so? Which minorities did you have in mind (e.g., ethnic minorities, socioeconomic minorities, gender-identity minorities, religious minorities)?"

Race:
A group of people descended from a common ancestor
having shared distinct physical characteristics

Race is a word that seems to be used less and less every day due to the increased awareness of its limitations. For years, there was an emphasis on forming people's identity based on their ancestral background, which often involved distinguishing people based on physical characteristics, such as their skin tone or the shape of their eyes, nose, lips, and hips. This has often contributed to people's tendency to hold very strong views of themselves in comparison to others, with values and beliefs attributed to those physical characteristics and biological ancestry. And while this tendency certainly continues to a lesser degree today, the increased prominence of DNA testing has brought awareness to the fact that there is little to no research that effectively supports the stereotypes attributed to ancestry-based distinctions between individuals' abilities and values.

In addition, DNA tests are revealing that most individuals are not 100 percent composed of their identified race, leading them to feel conflicted about the values and beliefs they attributed to "other people" after realizing they themselves share at least some ancestral lineage with those "other people." Some people even modify their self-view to better align with the values and beliefs they attribute to the ancestral background suggested in their DNA test results (e.g., "All my life I identified as German and disliked the Irish, until the test results revealed I was actually Irish and not German, so now I'll learn to be Irish").

In my therapeutic efforts, I always recommend that when people receive new and potentially identity-changing information, such as results from DNA tests, that they do so cautiously and deliberately. A healthy goal is to gain a greater appreciation for where we came from without having this knowledge dictate who we are and the direction we choose to take our lives. And if you see someone in your personal or professional life who is at a crossroads with new information about their background, I recommend that you supportively help them make a similar distinction—one of appreciation without dictation—so they can make healthier choices toward a sense of self.

Another limitation of the word and concept of *race* is the ongoing challenge of identifying the most appropriate terms of reference (e.g., White, European American, Caucasian). In doing this, we must consider the significance of these terms in practical daily use. Although the term *Caucasian* refers to having ancestors who traced back to the mountain of Caucus, I can't say that many people who use that term (either about themselves or others) are really seeking to convey that ancestry when they use the term. In light of the reality that ancestral lineage and physical characteristics are usually not the most significant factors we are trying to convey when we use a word like *race*, ethnicity offers a more relevant alternative.

> **Ethnicity:**
> The state of belonging to a social group
> that has common national cultural tradition

Unlike race, which focuses on ancestrally linked characteristics, ethnicity emphasizes the broader group identification that is often determined by physical as well as other characteristics, which together provide a descriptor that has more meaning in daily use. When someone utilizes words like "ethnicity" to describe you, they are more likely interested in the character traits and practices that connect you to a larger group, in which case gaining a better understanding of culture becomes very relevant.

> **Culture:**
> The behaviors, beliefs, and characteristics of a particular social,
> ethnic, or age group (i.e., the way of life of a certain people,
> including but not limited to family and societal roles, clothing,
> music, food, ceremonies, festivals, and holidays)

Culture is a word that is often used synonymously with race and ethnicity, and while it's related, it does not convey the same meaning. Someone could move from one geographic location to another, walk outside their new home, and say, "I like our new neighborhood. It has a lot of culture," and they would be conveying nothing that has to do with the racial or ethnic background of that neighborhood's population. Instead, they would be referring to the abundant variety of restaurants, museums, classic architecture, theater offerings, community festivals, and gatherings in that particular community. Culture describes the characteristics of a particular people or social group, but it does not specify the type of group being described.

In an effort to help distinguish between race, ethnicity, and culture, I recommend you consider the following oversimplification:

Race + Culture = Ethnicity

Ethnicity doesn't just convey a person's physical background; it also reflects the group they identity with and its impact on how they live their lives. However, until ethnicity becomes a more socially familiar term, you'll continue to see race and culture used synonymously, or you'll see categorical titles that suggest both, such as in the diversity wheel, which lists "race/ethnicity." Whichever word you choose, be intentional about your choice, and convey what and whom you are referring to as effectively as you can.

Views of Racism

Although the word *race* seems to be being used less and less in favor of *ethnicity,* the former will likely not disappear in use because it is so closely linked to this word: *racism.* We have to go no further than the Oxford Dictionary to see the following very clear and practical definition of racism:

> **Racism:**
> The belief that different races possess distinct characteristics, abilities, or qualities, especially so as to distinguish them as inferior or superior to one another

Racism is about conveying the message that a person or group of persons is better than another person or group of persons, primarily on the basis of their race. Whether expressed loudly or softly, directly or indirectly, intending to harm or not, if it conveys that message, then it can be included in a conversation of experiences of racism.

The *Reverse Racism* Dilemma

Now that we have a simple working definition of racism, it is worth addressing a related term that you may encounter in your broader multicultural awareness and diversity growth journey: *reverse racism.* There are multiple uses for this term, and there are varying perspectives and opinions that influence conversations about reverse racism. I will address two that are common and offer a challenge to consider a broader perspective that can help you converse considerately with others. Most importantly, I want you to be prepared in the event that a client reports having experienced reverse racism so you can better understand and empathize with them.

For some, reverse racism refers to the belief that since racism is about conveying the message that some people are superior or inferior to others based solely on their race, then racism is racism, and anyone can be racist.

REVERSE RACISM: RACISM IS RACISM

Consider... a group of people who identify as White Americans who are gathered across the room from a group of people who identify as African Americans. A random White individual calls out to a random African American and declares that people who are White are categorically better than African Americans. The African American individual responds by asserting that he does not appreciate being considered inferior and that he considers the assertion to be racist. He adds that not only was the comment not appreciated, but it was incorrect, as African Americans are clearly categorically better than White Americans. In response to this, the White individual says, "If it's racist when I say it, then it's racist when you say it."

The primary perspective in this use of the term is that if racism is about conveying beliefs about superiority and inferiority (as the most basic definition of the word implies) then anyone, regardless of their racial or ethnic background, can convey that belief.

There is, however, another use of the term *reverse racism* that is worth addressing. This perspective maintains that racism has an element of oppression, which requires a power differential that, at least in the United States, only applies to White Americans. Furthermore, this perspective asserts that no matter how similar the messages or actions may be, depending on who is sending the message, it's not the same and cannot be experienced the same way.

REVERSE RACISM: IT'S NOT THE SAME

Consider... an elementary school playground, where students play happily during a mid-day recess. During their play, the door to the school opens and out walks Big Billy, the school's number one bully. Although playground play continues, it occurs at a slightly slower pace as everyone, keenly aware of Big Billy's presence, awaits his chosen playground destination. They know that wherever Big Billy wants to be, they don't want to be because wherever he goes, he gets what he wants.

Billy scans the playground, makes his decision, and begins to walk toward the swing set where Little Johnny is swinging. Big Billy indicates that he wants the seat Little Johnny is on. Little Johnny is not delusional; he knows he is "Little" Johnny and that he is facing "Big" Billy, and the likely outcome if a physical altercation were to occur. As Big Billy approaches, Little Johnny surprises Big Billy by jumping off the swing in mid-air and kicking him. Big Billy doubles over onto the ground, writhing in pain. A teacher appears and sends both boys to the principal's office.

Big Billy blurts out, "Principal, principal, he bullied me! When I hit others, I'm called a bully! But this time, I didn't even do anything, and he hit me! He bullied me!" Hearing this, the principal turns to Little Johnny and says, "Little Johnny, you know that we don't support physical aggression in this school as a way to solve our problems or express our feelings." As Little Johnny leaves the room, Big Billy's satisfied grin grows large. But instead of releasing Big Billy to go on his way, the principal turns to him and says, "Now Big Billy, what Little Johnny did was not good, and as I mentioned, we don't support his actions. However, what he did was not bullying. You see, when you threaten with physical aggression, you have the ability to use the power of your threat to get your way and to make him feel small and powerless. This reduces the need for you to actually use your physical force and allows you to rely on intimidation instead. While it may seem the same, it's different."

This scenario describes an often-misunderstood aspect of racism: oppression. Although a little kid may express physical aggression when trying to beat up a big kid on a playground, it often doesn't have the same lasting impact as when the big kid does the same. Why? Because there isn't the power behind it that leads to ongoing experiences of oppression. Historical experiences in America have contributed to unequal distributions of power that have led to experiences of powerlessness and futility. Therefore, while anyone can express unhealthy beliefs of superiority and inferiority based on race, not everyone has the same power to influence others with their beliefs.

The goal here is not to promote or justify either of these definitions of reverse racism as right or wrong. Rather, it is to provide you with an understanding of the experiences behind these perspectives so if you encounter someone who expresses similar perspectives, you can be better prepared to offer empathy and understanding of their values (regardless of whether you share the same values), rather than unintentionally invalidating their perspective and negatively impacting your relationship with them.

But I Don't Think I'm Racist

Now armed with a practical, simple definition of racism—and with a glimpse into the subtle, nuanced, and legitimate perspectives that are included in racism-related conversations—it can be easy to see how many people differ in terms of what they consider to be racist. This is often so much the case that people genuinely don't know how to respond to accusations of racism. After all, if intent alone isn't the only criteria, then simply responding to being called racist with "No I'm not," because there wasn't racist intent, may result in accusations of defensiveness and invalidated feelings instead of mutual understanding. In order to help clarify perspectives on racism even further, I would like to offer the following practical use definitions:

> **Racism:**
> The belief that people of my racial group are better (i.e., of greater value, worth, importance, and/or skill) than people not in my racial group—whether this conveyed overtly or covertly, intentionally or unintentionally

Some people suggest that we live in a post-racial society by highlighting the absence of overt oppression in the form of slavery, as well as the lack of overt segregation in the form of Whites-only water fountains and other similar practices, rules, and policies. Others suggest that beliefs of superiority and inferiority remain strong and that what has really changed is how they are expressed. Racism may not be expressed and applied as openly as it once was, but evidence of more subtle expressions and applications remain.

As helping professionals, it is imperative that we make intentional efforts to assess our verbal and nonverbal communication to ensure we are reducing any indications of superiority or inferiority based on race (or any other criteria for that matter). Additionally, we need to be prepared to empathize with the experiences of racism by those we serve. We should not judge these racial experiences as "right" or "wrong" based on how we would feel if we were in the client's shoes. Instead, we should view it as a legitimate feeling based on their experiences. The goal is not to end with the application of a word like *racism* but to identify the source of undesirable experiences and reduce its impact on people's lives.

As we continue our discussion of commonly misunderstood terms, we must also consider the definition of *ethnocentrism*:

> **Ethnocentrism:**
> The belief that people like me are normal,
> while those unlike me are abnormal

Ethnocentrism highlights how people's differences are seen as abnormal or unusual. It's not necessarily that people have explored different ways of being and have come to the conclusion that their way is the best way. More often, it is that people are unaware of other ways of being and are operating as if their way is the only way.

THE SLEEPOVER REVELATION

Consider... a child who attends a sleepover at a friend's home for the first time. Once playtime has concluded and the mealtime and bedtime routine begins, this child becomes confused as the realization hits that mealtime and bedtime don't look the same at his friend's home as it does at his own home. He realizes for the first time that "the way" mealtime and bedtime is done at his home isn't "the way" it's done at his friend's home. This opens the door to lots of questions, such as "How many other ways are there to choose from?" and "Why do they do it that way in their home?"

This child's transition—from reasonable ignorance to a broadened perspective—is a heathy goal to strive for as it relates to encounters of ethnocentrism. In order to make this transition, we must first make intentional efforts to distinguish ethnocentrism from racism, and then we must respond with information rather than with judgment and defensiveness.

When someone views something as "abnormal," this is an acknowledgment that they have encountered something with which they are not familiar—something that is outside of their normal. Sometimes the question "Why do you do it that way?" isn't an accusation of wrongdoing but is a genuine query about something they have never considered before. If someone is open to learning about the world outside of their idea of normal, then make the most of the opportunity to inform their ignorance. Expand their perspective on a greater variety of normal, and you'll be planting seeds that can improve their interactions with everyone they encounter.

> **Cultural Pride:**
> Expressing a healthy appreciation of and value for one's own culture

In addition to variations in cultural backgrounds, there are also variations in how cultural values and ways of being are expressed. Culture has the potential to be a rarely expressed aspect of one person's identity, while for another person it is an essential aspect of their identity and self-worth. When differences in expression arise, there is the potential for a misinterpretation of the motivations behind those differences. A healthy sense of cultural pride may look, to some, very similar to racism and ethnocentrism. However, what motivates it is something entirely different.

A CULTURAL PRIDE MISUNDERSTANDING

Consider... an office filled with a maze of cubicles, where an American accountant walks through the maze to drop off a financial report to a Korean accountant. Upon returning to her cubicle, the American accountant says to her neighbor in the adjacent cubicle, "Can you believe that he's being so blatantly racist? He has decorated his cubicle with Korean art and photos, is playing Korean music, and is wearing Korean clothing."

Unbeknownst to the American accountant, the Korean accountant had come over from his cubicle to return a document he was mistakenly given. Having overheard the comment, he genuinely asks, "What makes you say that I'm being racist?" Slightly uncomfortable, the American responds, "We see you over there with your cubicle decorated that way, with your music playing so we all have to hear it, and with your clothes and hair styled that way. You're forcing your culture down our throat. It's obvious that you're doing all of that because you think you're better than we are. That your culture is better than ours."

The Korean accountant replies sincerely, "I'm sorry you feel that way, but I can assure you that I do not think that I am better than anyone. I am very proud of my culture and heritage, and I like to surround myself with reminders of my culture, but it's not in comparison to you or anyone else here."

The American says, "Well, you may not think you're better than we are, but you surely think that your way is the normal or right way and that our way is the wrong or abnormal way."

He replies, "Actually, I don't. I know that my way is the way that is normal for me, my family, and my community. I assume that your way is normal for you, your family, and your community."

Again, the American responds, "Well, maybe so, but it doesn't take all of that to express yourself. Why do you have to be so overt about it?"

The Korean ends by saying, "I can see how my way of expressing myself is more than what you are accustomed to, but that doesn't make it 'too much' any more than your way is 'not enough.' I feel that I have a healthy sense of cultural pride, and this is how I feel most comfortable expressing it. I am more than happy with you expressing your cultural background as much or as little as you desire."

When you encounter clients who are expressing their cultural background in a different manner than you are accustomed to, I challenge you to make intentional efforts to avoid judging them for being different. If being different was wrong, then your being different from them would be just as wrong. Instead, acknowledge your perspective as normal based on your experiences, and acknowledge someone else's perspective as normal based on their experiences. Then take steps to learn about differing experiences. You may be pleasantly surprised how doing so helps you reduce misunderstandings and strengthen relationships. The worksheet on the next page can assist you through this process so you can reduce unintentional offenses.

Reducing Unintentional Offenses

If someone reports feeling offended by something you have said or done, it can be easy to first defend your sincere and non-offensive intentions before considering whether or not there is any merit to the other person's feelings and experience of your words or actions. It is beneficial to remember that others' offended feelings do not necessarily mean you have done anything wrong. Rather, it may be more of a reflection of your behavior reminding them of past hurtful experiences they have had with others. It is also beneficial to consider that others' expressions of offense may help reveal subconscious beliefs you are unintentionally expressing.

Take a moment to explore some ways that you may be communicating your views of others and yourself in relation to others.

> **Microaggressions:**
> Subtle and often subconscious denigrating messages
> within brief everyday exchanges (e.g., when you offend
> others without intending to do so)

In what ways might I be unintentionally offending my clients or colleagues? What relational signs have I seen that may be an indication that I have unintentionally offended someone? How can I address the misunderstanding and begin to repair that relationship?

_____

_____

_____

_____

Racism: The belief that people like me are better (i.e., of greater value, worth, importance, and/or skill) than people not like me

In what ways might I be unintentionally communicating that I am better than someone else primarily because of the difference between our racial/ethnic backgrounds? What beliefs may I need to change in light of my increasing cultural empathy and understanding of people from various backgrounds? How might I communicate a different message in my daily interactions?

_____

_____

_____

_____

Ethnocentrism: The belief that people like me are normal, while others are abnormal

In what ways might I be unintentionally communicating that my way of doing things is normal, while the ways others from different racial/ethnic backgrounds do things is abnormal? What beliefs may I need to change in light of my increasing cultural empathy and understanding of people from various backgrounds? How might I communicate a different message in my daily interactions?

_____

_____

_____

_____

Cultural Pride: A healthy appreciation of and value for one's own culture

In what ways do I embrace a healthy appreciation of and value for my own cultural heritage? In what ways can I support others' varying expressions of healthy appreciation of their own cultural backgrounds?

_____

_____

_____

_____

Microaggressions

I will take the liberty of assuming that if you have made it this far in the book, you are not actively trying to be racist toward others. If, however, avoiding overt racism is not your biggest personal or professional struggle, then what is likely more relevant for you is the topic of microaggressions.

> **Microaggressions:**
> Brief, everyday exchanges that send denigrating messages to certain individuals because of their group membership; they are often subtle in nature and often occur automatically and unconsciously
> —Psychologist Derald Wing Sue

Unlike overt racism, microaggressions occur when you culturally offend others without meaning to do so. This often involves conveying a message about a belief you didn't intend to convey, but it also may or may not accurately describe what you actually feel or believe. Derald Wing Sue and David Sue (2013) list several examples of microaggressions in daily interactions. I will elaborate on just a few of them here.

Telling someone, "You are a credit to your race."

While this statement is very often intended to be a compliment directed at a person of color, it is often experienced as a microaggression. It almost compels the person to respond with, "Thanks for complimenting me and for insulting everyone in my community whom I care about." Although this message is intended to convey a sense of pleasant surprise on the speaker's behalf, it implies that the speaker expected something less from the person of color and from people like them. It is the *surprise* that often has the lasting effect more so than the *pleasant* intent.

Clutching a purse or wallet when a person of color approaches

Although you may not encounter certain behaviors during your daily encounters or even in your lifetime—such as crossing the street to avoid walking near someone or moving to the corner of an elevator when a certain cultural group gets on—that doesn't mean that more subtle gestures don't occur.

AN UNINTENTIONAL FIRST IMPRESSION

Consider... a client who sits in a waiting room before the start of his counseling session with a new therapist. After the therapist's previous client departs, the therapist walks with this client back to her office. As they both sit in their respective chairs, the therapist subtly moves her purse from the near side of the desk to the far side and then begins to initiate a conversation. However, for the client, life pauses for a moment. The client thinks, *I know I'm not your first client of the day because I saw your previous client leave. And I know I'm not your last client because it's the middle of the day. What made you feel the need in this moment to move your purse away from me?*

In this scenario, no words were even spoken, and yet a nonverbal message was conveyed: "People like you are generally criminals or otherwise cannot be trusted." When people are questioned about gestures like these, many defend their actions by asserting that it is obvious why they drew such conclusions. They convey that while they had no intention to offend, and that they hope to be pleasantly surprised by being wrong in having taken such precautions, they feel that their caution is reasonable based on seemingly common negative assumptions and beliefs about certain groups of people.

Helping professionals are not immune to occurrences such as these. In fact, my goal is not to even convince you of the rightness or wrongness of these kinds of actions. My goal is to encourage you to make intentional efforts to continually assess your assumptions and beliefs about others, including the support or lack of support you have for such assumptions and beliefs. And most importantly, I want to encourage you to make every effort to reduce the negative impact the expression of such assumptions can have on others.

Telling others, "I'm not a racist. I have several black friends."

This phrase is not only common, but it can also be substituted for a number of other attempted reassurances, such as "I'm not homophobic or heterosexist. I have a gay friend." While this message is intended to genuinely convey that someone is immune to racism or heterosexism, what it overlooks is the reality that the acknowledgement of differences does not guarantee that someone isn't prejudiced against individuals from those groups. At best, it reflects that there is room for an exception. In fact, that particular friend may feel conflicted and conclude, "You may like me, but you don't seem to like us."

Assuming people or persons of color are service workers

Being mistaken for a Target® employee when you happen to be shopping while wearing a red shirt may be inconvenient, but it's an understandable mistake with a clear reason for the misunderstanding (i.e., the red shirt). However, when persons of color are mistaken for wait staff at restaurants or for subordinates in business offices, when there is no other clear reason for the misunderstanding, it is reasonable for that person to take offense. In these cases, they can only conclude that the other person's assumption about them is likely due to perceptions that persons of color couldn't possibly occupy high-level positions.

The challenge here is not to be held back by shame if you find yourself or someone else making these assumptions. Rather, take a moment to explore what experiences contributed to those assumptions, and make efforts to modify them appropriately.

Mistaking the female doctor for a nurse

Not only are people prone to mistake people of color for service workers, but they also often hold the misguided notion that women cannot hold the same positions of power as men. Despite many changes that have occurred over several decades, men often hold the misguided notion that women only occupy supporting roles and cannot hold the same leadership positions as men. As helping professionals, we have the opportunity to help people expand their perspectives regarding the potential of those with whom they differ, and reduce the limiting assumptions they place on others.

EMERGENCY ROOM EMBARRASSMENT

Consider... a man who is admitted to an emergency room after an accident. After waiting a while to be seen, a woman walks into the room to check on him. As soon as she enters, the man expresses in exasperation, "Nurse, nurse, what's taking the doctor so long to get in here?" In response, the woman says, "First, I'm your doctor, not your nurse, so I would appreciate if you addressed me as such. Second, since I'm the one who will be operating on you, I'd recommend that you begin treating me with some respect."

Assuming the only two options for relationship
status are married and single

Just as there are patriarchal assumptions governing a woman's role in the workplace, there is also the common misconception that a person's relationship status can only be one of two options: single or married. An increasing awareness of other types of relationships—such as partners who choose not to be married, or same-sex couples in places where the government prohibits their civil marriage—necessitates increased flexibility in opportunities for relationship status descriptors in professional settings. While change may seem inconvenient, the potential benefits of validating identity and valuing relationships are priceless.

MORE THAN JUST A BOX

Consider... a man who goes into a mental health clinic to meet his therapist for the first time. He approaches the front desk, where an administrative assistant hands him a clipboard with some initial paperwork to complete prior to the start of his session. He takes the clipboard to a seat in the waiting room and begins filling out the forms. A few lines in, he returns to the front desk to address a concern and says, "Ma'am, I'm sorry to bother you, but I have a question about one of the lines on this form. You see, it asks for my relationship status, with options for married or single, and you see the way my relationship works is—"

The assistant cuts him off and says with a reassuring tone, "Are you married?" A little put off by being interrupted, he responds, "No, I'm not." The assistant then asserts, "Then just check the box that says single, and you can explain the details to your therapist when your session starts." The man thinks to himself, *Just check single? And minimize my several-year-long relationship? Not even acknowledge my lifelong commitment?*

Sometimes microaggressions can occur before you even meet the person you are intending to serve in one form or another. Messages like these, whether in person or in documentation, can convey that LGBTQ+ partnerships don't matter and are meaningless. It is in your best interest to explore your words and your supporting forms, brochures, and website information to look for language that may potentially minimize experiences and identities different from your own.

Staring at two men holding hands in public

Relatedly, individuals in the LGBTQ+ community frequently encounter microaggressions when they exhibit displays of affection that would otherwise be considered "normal" for heterosexual couples. As helping professionals, it is vital that we make intentional efforts to see and empathize with the reasonable frustrations that result from being seen as abnormal. We can start by increasing our self-awareness and reducing the likelihood that we are perpetuating unappreciated assumptions such as these based on perceived differences.

PDA IN THE PARK

Consider... a large city park, where a man, woman, and child are enjoying quality time together on a picnic blanket in the grass. After a while, they notice two men walking together on a nearby path, casually holding hands and having just given each other a peck on the cheek. As they pass by, the man on the blanket politely asks the gentlemen if they wouldn't mind keeping their public displays of affection private, as the man and woman aren't yet ready to teach their child about same-sex relationships.

Now flip it: Same park. Same picnic blanket. On the blanket are two men and a child, enjoying quality time together. After a while, they notice a man and a woman walking together on a nearby path, casually holding hands and having just given each other a peck on the cheek. As they pass by, one of the gentlemen on the blanket politely asks the man and woman walking by if they wouldn't mind keeping their public displays of affection private, as the men aren't yet ready to teach their child about heterosexual relationships.

While many who hear the first half of this scenario experience a sense of disrespect and insensitivity at the parents' request, others only see it as a reasonable request that was expressed politely and with no reason for concern. Interestingly, however, many individuals who view the request as reasonable in the first scenario do not consider it to be reasonable in the second scenario. Without arguing for or against the reasonableness of anyone's actions and personal identities, I suggest that when you ask someone to hide their identity because others might find it offensive, it doesn't matter how politely you express this request. That person will still experience your request in the same manner and will likely feel denigrated by the experience.

White Guilt: Removing the Shame

As we explore differences between racism and microaggressions, it is beneficial to consider their internal and relational implications. There is often a tendency for White Americans to choose between two extremes of either strongly *embracing* or strongly *resisting* the guilt associated with America's past treatment of particular ethnic cultural groups—namely African Americans and the history of slavery, Native Americans and the history of genocide, and Japanese Americans and the history of internment camps.

Sometimes these internal dilemmas get expressed in our day-to-day interactions, with very sorrowful expressions, such as "I'm sorry for everything that my ancestors did to your ancestors, and if there is anything that I can do to help make up for those injustices, feel free to let me know" or "Look, I wasn't a slave owner. You weren't a slave. That was over a hundred years ago. So let's live in the present because that has nothing to do with us today."

I must admit that this is not an easy dilemma to solve. Living with the guilt of actions you have never done—by individuals you have never known—seems to be more damaging than helpful. At the same time, denying any impact of the past on the present seems more damaging than helpful as well. If both of these have merit, then the challenge remains to find a healthy state of being somewhere in middle.

To address this dilemma, author Tim Wise offers a few suggestions about how to think about White guilt that may lead to a healthier, less extreme resting point. He explains that *guilt* is what you feel in response to something you have done (Michigan Roundtable for Diversity and Inclusion, 2010). If you didn't actively or passively engage in the action in question, then guilt is not the most appropriate feeling. Sure, the past matters, and while a symbolic gesture of apology on behalf of someone else may have benefits, apologizing out of genuine personal guilt for something that someone else did in the past has little relational benefit in the present (for either party).

Responsibility, on the other hand, may be a more appropriate feeling in this situation. You can choose to take responsibility for the reality of the present, as well as the influence of the past on the present reality, because of the kind of person you are. Tim Wise likens the dilemma to that of environmental pollution. You may not have originally caused the pollution that exists today, but someone did (in the past), a legacy exists (which influences the present), and today we have a responsibility to take care of the environment that was handed down to us.

A TALE OF TWO VILLAGES

Consider... a large remote wooded area where there are two villages. Although the two villages are miles apart and don't yet know of each other's existence, they share the use of a river that runs through both villages. One village is upstream, and the other is downstream. Both villages are small and filled with hardworking people who are raising their families, building their communities, and farming the land to meet all of their needs.

An individual in the village upstream has a bright idea to build a small industrial facility that, while mostly helping to produce better crops, also unintentionally produces some waste that pollutes the water supply heading downstream. The village upstream doesn't realize it is producing anything negative and doesn't even know the other village exists.

Life goes on, and over the years both villages grow. The villages grow into towns, the towns grow into cities, and generations come and go. After a number of years, the industrial facility closes down and is no longer in use. Although no new pollution is being added to the water downstream, the soil used for farming and growing the crops has been forever impacted.

Eventually, boundaries are expanded such that the two cities discover each other. And as they learn more about each other, several similarities and differences become evident.

On the one hand, they both have similar family and community relationships and structures, as well as similar values for hard work, especially with regard to farming. On the other hand, the crops grown upstream are larger, firmer, and juicier than those grown downstream. They logically conclude that this difference must be the result of superior farming techniques. However, after a sincere effort to teach the downstream community the upstream way of farming, they don't see significant improvement and begin to wonder whether the downstream community is following through on their farming instructions. What they don't realize is that the soil used by the downstream community is not the same as that used by the upstream community. While the source of the pollution that originally caused the change has been eliminated, the soil is forever altered.

Similarly, the upstream community begins to notice that despite having similar values for health and well-being, they are healthier and stronger than the downstream community. They logically conclude that this difference must be the result of superior exercise techniques. However, after a sincere effort to teach the downstream community the upstream way of exercising, they don't see significant improvement and began to wonder whether the downstream community is somehow not following through on their exercising instructions. What they don't realize is that the food and water consumed by the downstream community is not the same as the food and water consumed by the upstream community, and no amount of positive exercise can eliminate the negative impact of past actions on present realities.

My question to you is this: Should those in the upstream community feel guilty about their current state of living when they realize that their ancestors contributed to the discrepancy? Similarly, should the those in the downstream community be angry and demand apologies from those currently living upstream, despite the fact that those who directly contributed to these troubles have long since passed away, leaving only blame and resentment for those whose only fault was having grown up with different opportunities?

Given that guilt is an appropriate feeling in response to one's own actions, it would be misguided for the upstream community to feel guilty in this case. However, it *is* reasonable for them to take responsibility for the opportunities they have today so they can reduce the unfortunate discrepancies that nonetheless exist. When it comes to privilege, there needs to be a way to address the advantages that some people, but not others, have in a way that gives appropriate legitimacy to the feelings and needs of those on both sides of this discrepancy. This is where a healthy perspective on privilege becomes beneficial.

Privilege

Privilege is a term that describes advantages available to certain individuals or groups. To gain a practical understanding of privilege in daily life, let's take a look at Peggy McIntosh's article "White Privilege: Unpacking the Invisible Knapsack" (1988). In it, she seeks to bring attention to the reality of White privilege—the idea that White Americans have opportunities and advantages that non-White Americans do not benefit from. She acknowledges that she is not only introducing a new concept to some, but she is also addressing those who argue that White privilege doesn't exist. Many who argue against the existence of White privilege explain with sincerity that they are not privileged since they do not feel privileged, they don't possess significant financial capital or political influence, and they don't get whatever they want just because of the color of their skin. In response to these claims, McIntosh chooses instead to begin with a more provable privilege comparison: male privilege.

Male Privilege

We need to look no further than the wage gap to find tangible support for male privilege in America. A 2019 PayScale report showed that women earn just 79 cents for every dollar men make. According to McIntosh, this reflects a male privilege that is unearned, unacknowledged, denied, taken for granted, and protected.

Unearned. One cannot argue that men make more than women because they have better credentials prior to employment and work harder once they're on the job. That's because the wage gap remains consistent even when considering various factors, such as identical job titles, role expectations, previous experience, and job performance. Despite the numerous similarities in factors worthy of earning, men make more than women on average.

Unacknowledged. Despite the fact that the wage gap is not a new phenomenon, most men aren't consciously aware of its existence, let alone the impact of this inequality on women. Most men are not living day to day callously thinking or saying, "Yep, I know I make more. Not my problem."

Denied. Given that men rarely give conscious consideration to the wage gap, they often deny its existence. Since they live day to day without the experience of gender inequality and do not have to be confronted with it, many disagree that it exists when someone else brings it to their attention and expresses that it has been a problem. This isn't because men want to invalidate someone else's experience and feelings. Rather, it's an effort to make sense of their perspective of the world in which they live. Many genuinely respond by expressing, "What? That can't be. You see, I know a woman in my field who holds the same position as I do in a different company across town, and she makes a few cents more than I do. So there, I just disproved male privilege and the wage gap all at once." Unfortunately, this only highlights an exception, rather than the rule.

Taken for granted. Even when men acknowledge the wage gap and admit to their privilege, many dismiss the urgency to take action on solving the problem. They may express things such as "Okay, I see your point. Men make more than women, even when other things are equal. But some men get paid more and others get paid less. Things change all the time. I'm sure things will just work out in the end. Just wait and see. There's no need to make a big deal out of it." This statement perfectly reflects the concept of male privilege because men have the privilege to not worry about the wage gap and thus have less incentive to change the situation. They can take it for granted.

Protected. Many men respond to an increased awareness and understanding of wage inequality with a protective stance. They may say, "Although I have a greater appreciation for the dilemma women face, and while I think it would be great if you made more, the company where I work has a fixed amount of revenue, and in order for you to get paid more, I would need to get paid less, and I didn't do anything wrong to deserve a pay cut. So while I hope you are able to find a solution to your problem, I'm sorry, but I can't be a part of that solution because I have to protect what I have."

A Broader Perspective on Privilege

The discussion on male privilege highlights how privilege isn't necessarily about socioeconomic or political power and influence in society, nor is it necessarily about someone's entitled perspective on life. Rather, privilege is having the luxury to not be concerned about things that others are concerned about. In this perspective, there can be many kinds of privilege: ethnic privilege, gender privilege, age privilege, socioeconomic privilege, and so on. McIntosh elaborates that what is common between them is that they reflect advantages for some that—in an equal world—would be societal norms. As it relates to ethnic privilege, McIntosh posits that **many individuals are taught how racism puts others at a disadvantage, without realizing that it puts them at an advantage**.

People do not need behave in a negative manner or have negative intentions for this advantage or privilege to exist. Even more so, when privilege is experienced as oppressive, much of that oppression is subconsciously enacted on the part of the person with privilege. Not only is privilege often unintentional, but it is also unseen, which makes it difficult to address. To bring about change, McIntosh challenges us to reveal privilege where it exists and to motivate those who have it to give up some of it.

Now I recognize that the phrase "give up some of it" makes some people nervous when they read it, and it may generate a protective stance. But let me be clear: The desire and need to protect what we have is a legitimate feeling. However, we need to go no further than the recent discussion on male privilege and the wage gap to show that this protective stance is genuine but misguided. For while there is merit to the belief that men may need to get paid less in order for women to get paid more—as in the case of the company with the fixed revenue—there is also the possibility that men can become allies to the cause. They can help find solutions that allow companies to generate more financial resources for the sole purpose of allocating them to women to make things fairer and more equal. In this case, what men would be giving up is not their income but the gap itself—the financial lead that they unjustifiably hold ahead of women.

Privilege in the Real World

Before we leave the discussion of privilege, I want to take a moment to explore some of the ways privilege can be seen in daily interactions. McIntosh offers 26 examples to assist in this effort. Here, I'll elaborate on just a few of them.

I can turn on a television or open up the front page of a newspaper and see people of my race widely represented.

When some people encounter media such as *BET* (*Black Entertainment Television*) or *People en Español* (*People Magazine* in Spanish), they ask questions, such as "Why do they have to have their own magazines, television stations, and movies? Why can't they just watch the regular television stations and the regular movies and read the regular magazines? Why do they have to be so exclusive?" And the answer is because while watching and reading those media venues is just fine, there is something significant about seeing yourself represented in media venues such as these. And unfortunately, many of the "regular" venues don't reflect the diversity of their viewership.

In addition, there has historically been a pattern where individuals from ethnic minority backgrounds try to model for the "regular" magazines, be anchors on the "regular" news stations, and audition to act in the "regular" movies—only to be told that while the interview or audition was nice, they don't quite fit the part. And after hearing these types of responses repeatedly, some have decided to create their own magazines, television stations, shows, and movies. It's interesting when critics or media executives are pleasantly surprised when movies with a predominately ethnic minority cast do exceedingly well in the box office, expressing, "Wow, you guys are really good actors, directors, etc." And the response is a polite and respectful, "Thanks. We know. You're the only one surprised. We've been trying to tell you that for years. But we're glad you can finally see it." People in the ethnic majority have the privilege of not even having to worry about the struggle to be seen because they have the privilege of seeing people like themselves reflected everywhere they look.

I can go shopping alone, and I won't be followed or harassed.

When my wife and I were pregnant with our first daughter and were out at a store shopping for baby clothes, we weren't in the store long before we realized that we had a shadow—a store employee nearby being suspiciously unproductive. Thinking little of it, we continued to shop, only to soon notice that despite the fact that we had transitioned to another location in the store, we had the same shadow. Now, because I am an optimistic person not wanting to jump to conclusions, I chose to assume that this store employee happened to finish whatever task they were doing in the first section of the store, and this happened to be the next section on their task list.

Eventually, we transitioned to a third section of the store, only to see the same store employee again. I then told my wife, "I'll be right back," and I made my way through several sections of the store in a random zigzag pattern and ended at a random unrelated section, only to find the same store employee appear soon after. It was then that I dropped the subtleties, walked directly to the store employee, and said, "Since you plan to follow me around the entire store, make yourself useful by holding these clothes, and you can be my shopping cart for the day." Now, let me be completely honest, this last confrontational part happened only in my head. In reality, I shook my head at the subtlety-free situation, my wife and I left, and we haven't returned to that store since.

There are those who, upon hearing this story, state with sincerity that maybe the store had experienced some shoplifting recently that had caused them to be a little overcautious. To this I say, "Maybe... but are they cautious about everyone who comes in the store or just some people? I wasn't the only patron of that establishment that day." I seek not to tarnish anyone's reputation (hence my not revealing the name of the store) but, instead, to highlight the fact that some people have the privilege to not worry about this experience, while others do not have that luxury.

I can go into a barber or hairdresser's shop and find someone who can cut my hair.

Shortly after I graduated from high school on the south side of Chicago, I left home to immerse myself in a new community: the large, predominately White community at the University of Minnesota. After a few weeks of getting adjusted to my new home, I got on the city bus headed off campus on a journey to find my next barber somewhere in the Twin Cities. As I rode on that bus, I sat by the window looking for the classic barber signal: the red, blue, and white barber pole. And as the bus passed by several businesses with this telltale sign, I looked in the windows to see who was cutting hair. In response to what I saw over and over again, I can admit that my not-yet-very-culturally sensitive mind thought, *That old White guy probably doesn't know how to do a high and tight bald fade.* I could have been wrong, but I wasn't at a place in my life where I was willing to risk it. As disappointment began to sink in while I scanned these windows, I saw a big sign that read, "Mr. Afros." I didn't have an afro, but I quickly concluded that there was a high likelihood that an establishment that knew how to cut afros would know how to give me a bald fade.

Today, the barber I trust to cut my hair is someone I respect personally and professionally. I trust him because of his proven professional skill in cutting my hair, and I also appreciate that I can enter his barber shop on any given day and see individuals in his barber chair representing various ethnicities, ages, and genders. I appreciate that he has made an intentional effort to become trained in how to cut a variety of hair textures. Many don't have the luxury of having someone they can trust like this, or if they do, they have to travel far outside of their community to find it. In contrast, other people have the privilege of just going to the barber or salon closest to them and having a pretty good chance that the professionals there will know how to cut or style their hair.

I can find bandages and makeup in colors that match my skin.

I applaud Band-Aid® for removing "flesh"–colored from their advertising of their peach-toned adhesive bandages, as they realized and were willing to acknowledge that their product didn't reflect the flesh color of all their customers. Similarly, I applaud Crayola® for removing "flesh" off the side of the crayon now simply identified as peach for the same reason. Not only that, but following the lead of a less popular crayon maker who made a specialty "people of color" pack, Crayola created their own multicultural pack of crayons specifically offering eight shades of brown.

For therapists working with children, there is a potential benefit to products such as these because it makes it easier to affirm a child's cultural self-identity when you instruct them to draw a picture of their family. Instead of having to choose between black, peach, and brown crayons, a child from a multiethnic background can choose among various options—allowing them to pick one shade for their father, another shade for their mother, a different shade for a sibling, and even another shade for their self-portrait. This allows the child's culture to be affirmed and validated. Many others have the privilege to not worry about this issue, choosing the peach crayon and moving on to other more personally relevant concerns.

Similar to the issue of crayon color is the topic of makeup. For example, my wife once asked me to pick up a type of foundation at the drugstore for her. Armed with the makeup brand, type, and color number, I located the cosmetics section of the store, identified the correct brand's section of items, and found the shelf for the product. I went in search of the correct color number, looking high and low, but it was nowhere to be found. When I asked for help from a store employee, I was told that they didn't carry the complete line. Was this a sign of intentional discrimination against certain cultural groups? Potentially.

However, when I inquired further, I was informed that when the makeup product line was first made available years earlier, this store purchased and stocked the entire line. Unfortunately, over time, the darker colors were not purchased very much (likely due to the demographics of that geographic region), causing the products to expire and leading the store to not repurchase the darker products. While this was inconvenient for those interested in purchasing those darker makeup products, it was a reasonable business decision—not racism—that gave certain customers privilege when it came to the available makeup selection in the store. Despite this reasonable motivation, other customers unfortunately don't share that privilege and instead have the inconvenience of either settling for less effective products or traveling outside of their community to meet their needs.

I can be sure that my children will be given toys featuring people of my race and curriculum materials that testify to the existence of my race.

When my oldest daughter was preparing to enter preschool, my wife and I accompanied her to a preschool open house. During the open house, we received a tour of the room, including the individualized cubbies, play area, craft and supplies area, and classroom library from which the read-aloud books were chosen. One of the things I found most interesting during the tour was that the children's books featured characters from a variety of cultural backgrounds. I later found out that the school made an intentional effort to expose the children to diversity so they would feel seen and represented and also to increase the likelihood of positive interactions with those they encountered in real life from various cultural backgrounds.

While this was not a prerequisite for us in choosing a preschool, it was definitely one that we appreciated. Sadly, some students experience years of formal education before they realize that people who look like them can be main characters, heroes, or even authors of significant books. And yet many other students have the privilege of frequently seeing people who look like them and don't know what it feels like to long to see themselves represented in a positive way.

Similarly, many people take toys for granted. The 1940s doll test (Clark & Clark, 1941/1958) revealed a tendency for African American children to see lighter skin-toned dolls as good and pretty, and darker skin-toned dolls as bad and ugly. I wish that this reality ended in the 1940s, but a few years ago, I had the pleasure of providing counseling services for the mother of a young African American daughter who had requested her first doll for Christmas. This mother saw an opportunity to affirm her daughter's cultural identity by choosing a doll whose skin tone reflected her daughter's. That way, her daughter could see some part of herself in the doll. However, the mother was devastated when her daughter unwrapped her doll and expressed, "Aw, I was hoping to get a pretty one." Ouch. I was challenged to help this mother wrestle with questions of uncertainty regarding the significance of her daughter's expression on her sense of self-esteem and self-identity. Many parents have the privilege of going to their closest store and finding an aisle or two of dolls that look in one way or another like their child.

I can criticize our government and talk about how much I fear its policies without being seen as a cultural outsider.

I have had the pleasure of traveling several times per year to facilitate trainings, workshops, and seminars around the country. In doing so, I have gone through my fair share of airport security checkpoints. And while I wait in these airport security lines, I mentally and emotionally prepare myself for the chance that I will be randomly selected to step to the side for a more personalized pat-down experience—and it has happened on several occasions. There have also been several occasions when I consider myself to be privileged compared to another man in line who appears to be from a Middle Eastern background as reflected by his skin tone, facial features, and clothing. Compared to him, I'm the privileged one, for while I may be inconvenienced in some ways, he has to watch everything he says and does (e.g., tempering his mannerisms, paying attention to whom he may look at for too long) all because of the actions of individuals whom he doesn't know and doesn't agree with.

And while there are definitely limits for anyone in environments like these, many others in that line have significantly more flexibility in what they say and do than this man does. Some respond to this realization by expressing that this Middle Eastern man, and others like him, should understand why people are uncomfortable. Unfortunately, it is a difficult argument to suggest that someone who personally did nothing wrong, and has no affiliation or shared belief with those who did, should accept and support the fear and potential judgment that is directed their way. And yet many others have the privilege of not being automatically compared with the worst associations of others because of unrelated similarities they share. **This is a great example of how privilege is not limited to Black and White; it can be experienced in various forms**.

I can use checks, credit cards, or cash and count on my skin color not to work against the appearance of my financial reliability.

Many ethnic minority customers have had the experience of being asked to show identification when utilizing checks at certain retail establishments—to prove they are who they say they are or out of fear that the check might bounce—only to realize that other customers have the privilege of not being inconvenienced this same way. Similarly, many ethnic minority customers have described receiving uncomfortable looks from retailers when they choose to pay with cash and pull out a large fold of bills when paying. They are given looks that suggest that a person from an ethnic minority who has "a large wad of cash" is suspicious, may have gained that money immorally, or isn't financially stable enough to maintain a credit card. However, other customers who choose to pay with cash (even in large bills) may not receive the same looks or have negative assumptions made about them. In fact, retailers are more likely to assume that this person doesn't need to pay with check or credit because they are so successful. Many have the privilege of not being concerned about this discrepancy because they are not personally inconvenienced by it.

I can do well in a challenging situation without being seen as a credit to my race.

Many individuals from ethnic minority backgrounds admit to having experienced additional stressors in difficult situations, such as applying for jobs or loans, because they have to be prepared to show their accomplishments and abilities, and they also feel compelled to not look or sound like the worst stereotypes about people who look like them. Oftentimes, this is not because they desire to hide something but because those stereotypes don't actually reflect them personally. However, there is an often unprovable but nonetheless supported belief that anything they say, do, or wear could be misinterpreted by someone else, which can limit their opportunities and make it difficult for those who may come after them to get a fair chance.

Just as one person's actions can pave the way and open the door for others to have similar opportunities, so can one person's actions make things more difficult. This is evident when individuals from various minority backgrounds are watching a breaking news report regarding someone who committed a crime, and before the suspect is identified, the person watching the report whispers repeatedly to themselves, "Please don't let it be someone like us." They're not afraid that they will actually know the suspect but, instead, are concerned that the perceptions of those watching will have a much broader negative impact.

On the contrary, it is less common for individuals who identify as White Americans to watch the news, hear of a suspect in a crime who also identifies as White, and then conclude, "Aw man, that's going to make things more difficult for me at work because I have to go out of my way to distance myself from being associated with people like that." Some people have the privilege of not being defined by bad choices of individuals in their cultural group.

I am never asked to speak for all the people in my racial group.

I once had an experience that caught me off guard while I was taking a graduate school course. It wasn't traumatizing by any means, but it was enlightening. During the lecture, the professor arrived at a discussion point where he expressed, "I wonder how those from ethnic minority backgrounds experience this topic." As I listened and took notes, curious as to what insight I would gain next, it took me a moment to realize that the professor had stopped talking and was looking at me—the apparent representative for ethnic minorities in the room. Not only that, but the rest of the heads in the class had swiveled from the professor to also look at me, in eager anticipation for me to pick up the proverbial mic and respond to the professor's indirect invitation to answer the question.

Those who know me know that I appreciate opportunities to inform ignorance. Their eyes communicated a desire to reduce their ignorance, and I refused to pass up such a receptive opportunity. I shared some experiences, acknowledging the limitations of my knowledge and experiences, but I also realized that my limited experiences were still greater than that what many of them had been exposed to. Then I gave the proverbial mic back to the professor and the lecture continued.

That being said, you should not assume that every individual from a minority background will respond similarly. Sometimes people reasonably resent being asked to speak for all people of their community, especially as the request may imply that one person's experience summarizes the experiences of the entire community. Sometimes your genuine, reasonable question is not appreciated because while it may be new to you, it's the 50th time the other person has been asked this same question. Other times, individuals from ethnic minority backgrounds may be cautious about answering questions and sharing their experience because when they have, their response was misunderstood, judged, or used to somehow negatively impact others.

The solution to this challenge is not to never ask questions but to be aware of and acknowledge the potential impact of your question, the limitations of the other person's answer, and your willingness to genuinely hear whatever answer they choose to give—even if that's no answer at all. Conveying this level of humility and genuineness can significantly increase the likelihood of a mutually beneficial interaction and can potentially reduce ignorance.

Regarding the role of privilege in my example, it is unlikely that anyone else in that room has been in any scenario, let alone multiple scenarios, where someone has asked, "I wonder how those from an ethnic majority cultural background feel about this subject matter," and the entire room has looked at them. They have not experienced the internal conflict of wanting to inform ignorance but also not knowing whether their response will be well-received or judged. It is a privilege to not have this continual concern.

If a traffic cop pulls me over, I can be sure that I wasn't singled out because of my race.

In recent years, social media has brought attention to the disproportionate experiences of police aggression toward individuals from ethnic minority backgrounds. While much is still unknown about the factors that contributed to these devastating events, the frequency with which they occur and the consequences that often result—namely, the loss of life at the hands of law enforcement officers—justify the abundance of caution that ethnic minority individuals take regarding potential encounters with law enforcement professionals.

Now let me clear, not all law enforcement professionals equally contribute to these trends. There are many who are in the field of law enforcement for good reasons, who come in with a healthy perspective, and who are similarly disturbed by the trends and desire to avoid contributing to those trends as much as possible. However, there are also many in our society who dismiss and minimize the concerns of ethnic minority individuals.

A common argument is "If you have done nothing wrong, you should have nothing to worry about." However, there have been multiple scenarios where evidence has shown that the victims did nothing to earn such mistreatment, which gives merit to the concern. Another common argument is "Well, those were rare, isolated incidents—not a common occurrence." However, given that we have found no definitive correlation between cause and effect in these incidents, it is understandable when someone states they don't want to be the next "rare, isolated incident."

After a widely publicized incident of extreme use of force by law enforcement that resulted in the loss of life of an unarmed African American victim, there was significant talk from politicians, journalists, celebrities, and talk show hosts exploring what the appropriate responses should be to incidents such as these. While some called for more punitive accountability in the form of immediate dismissal, others called for more lenient accountability, such as paid leave and additional training. To those who felt more punitive efforts were warranted, recommendations of paid time off and additional training felt insufficient and even disrespectful considering the loss of life involved. Sheryl Underwood, an African American woman and co-host of *The Talk*, expressed this sentiment well when she stated, "You don't have to train the police not to shoot White people. Why you got to train them not to shoot us?"

When people are driving and hear the high-pitched *whoop whoop* of a police car siren, there are various initial thoughts they may have. Some immediately look down at their speedometer and ask themselves, *Was I speeding?* Others think, *Did I run a red light that I thought was still yellow? Did I drive past a stop sign I didn't see? Is my taillight out?* In contrast, ethnic minority drivers are more likely to have initial thoughts like *Is it because of my skin color? Am I going to be told that I fit the description of someone they're looking for?* They are also more likely to ask themselves, *Will I still be alive in 10 minutes? I hope the officer isn't so afraid of me that a random movement results in the impossible-to-be-proved and later-to-be-justified taking of my life.* Regardless of the reasons you may believe these events occur, the reality is that many ethnic minority individuals experience reasonable fear that the worst could happen. Others have the privilege of not having to worry as much or at all.

I can take a job with an affirmative action employer without having coworkers on the job suspect that I got it because of my race.

An individual from an ethnic minority background who participates in a job interview but doesn't get the job might ask themselves, *Was it because of my race? Was I more qualified for the job than other interviewees but not truly considered because I didn't fit the office environment?* Given the ambiguous nature of many discriminatory efforts, which do not necessarily involve a clearly overt dismissive word or action, it can be difficult to know for sure whether it is a legitimate question or cultural paranoia.

This line of reasoning works the opposite way as well. An individual from an ethnic minority background who participates in a job interview and *does* get the job might ask themselves, *Was it because of my race? Did I really outshine every other candidate, or are they just trying to meet a quota or diversify the company photo?* Again, employers don't need to overtly display discriminatory practices for the job applicant to feel this way and for their concern to have reasonable validity. Research has shown that discriminatory hiring practices are frequent.

This job-related privilege also extends beyond ethnic minority status. Some wrestle with whether they were hired because of their gender, socioeconomic status, or age. The goal of affirmative action is not give a handout to underrepresented groups by engaging in reverse discrimination and exclusion. Rather, it is to give underrepresented groups of people a fair chance to be seen and appreciated.

Nonetheless, proof and percentages are not relevant here. The fact that some people have to ask themselves these questions at all is what is relevant. There are many who have the privilege to not have this concern and who rarely feel compelled to ask whether they were excluded or included because of their ethnic identity.

As you can see, while White privilege may be the most common and pressing issue to address for many, it is definitely not the only privilege that is experienced. From male privilege and socioeconomic privilege to heterosexual and cisgender privilege, we must acknowledge the reality that there are experiences and opportunities that some people have that are not as readily available to others. Once we acknowledge this reality, we can more effectively validate the feelings caused by those experiences and help people feel seen. We can also join together in taking steps toward a healthy solution.

A Perspective on Multicultural Competence

Similar to my earlier discussion regarding commonly misunderstood diversity-related terms, I would like to address various aspects of what is meant by the term multicultural *competence*. There are many definitions of multicultural competence, some common considerations of which include:

- **Knowledge:** Learning about another group's cultural history, traditions, values, and so on
- **Awareness:** Opening our eyes to the experiences of others
- **Understanding:** Incorporating newly acquired knowledge and awareness into our overall broader worldview and personal perspective
- **Practice/skills:** Putting learned knowledge and understanding into action in a way that promotes healthy relationship interactions
- **Social justice:** Putting knowledge, understanding, and awareness into practice in a way that improves the lives of those in our larger community; speaking up for and advocating for those who are unacknowledged or unfairly treated
- **Self-awareness:** Understanding that the better we know and understand ourselves, the more effective we can be in our efforts to understand and help others

- **Attitudes/beliefs:** Allowing new information to positively influence our attitudes and values about ourselves, others, and the world as a whole, including our thoughts and feelings and how those thoughts and feelings are reflected outwardly in our verbal and nonverbal communication
- **Self-confidence:** An increased confidence that we can reduce the likelihood of unintentional offenses and increase the likelihood of strengthened cultural relationships

Use the worksheet on the next page to reflect on your multicultural competence journey by considering your own experience of privilege, looking for the presence of microaggressions, and evaluating how you can respond to racism. Then take the cultural self-assessment to explore how you can grow and make improvements in the application of multicultural competence.

Cultural Competency Journey Reflection

In what ways is my current environment **diverse**, and in what ways can I benefit from an increase in diverse perspectives?

_____

_____

_____

In what ways do I experience **privilege** that others around me may not share?

_____

_____

_____

How can I look for potential **microaggressions** (expressed by me or anyone else) in order to decrease the likelihood of repeated unintentional offenses?

_____

_____

_____

When I see or hear an accusation of **racism** (toward me or anyone else), what types of questions can I ask myself to help me evaluate whether it is in fact racism? And how do I respond either way?

_____

_____

_____

Multicultural Competence Assessment

Multicultural competence involves more than learning the history of particular cultural groups. While gaining knowledge is beneficial, so is increasing your self-awareness and other-awareness; evaluating your personal beliefs, attitudes, and understanding; and looking for opportunities to develop self-confidence in the application of multicultural competence skills and effective practices in areas such as social justice.

Take a moment to explore areas of strength, as well as areas of potential growth, as they relate to your multicultural competence journey.

Step 1:

Rank the following multicultural competence skills in terms of strength and growth areas, with 1 being your greatest strength and 10 being your greatest growth area.

Step 2:

Explore ways in which you can make personal improvements in each area.

_____ Awareness _____

_____

_____ Self-Awareness _____

_____

_____ Beliefs _____

_____

_____ Knowledge _____

_____

_____ Understanding _____

_____

_____ Attitudes   _____
                         _____

_____ Skills   _____
                         _____

_____ Practice   _____
                         _____

_____ Social Justice   _____
                         _____

_____ Self-Confidence   _____
                         _____

Multicultural Competence Is a Journey, Not a Destination

As in many other areas of life, cultural competence is a journey, not a destination. It is less about whether you know as much as someone else does and more about your willingness to learn more as you have opportunities to do so.

Consider this picture of a yellow brick road.

Instead of the expected picture of the ultimate destination of Oz at the end of that road, there is simply a horizon. But what do you see when you get to the end of the bricks on the yellow brick road depicted here? More bricks. The road keeps going. Down a hill. Up a hill. Maybe it winds a bit. On this multicultural awareness and competence journey, it is beneficial to focus less on identifying the end goal of the "right" amount of knowledge, the "right" amount of skills, and the "right" amount of practice. It is not about how far along the road you are in comparison to others or even to your own expectations about where you "should" be. Rather, it is about asking yourself if you are *on the road* to cultural competence.

Not everyone is on the road. Some are content to sit beneath the trees on the side of the road. Although they may have had experiences that have helped them along the road, they are content with staying where they are, without feeling the need to learn more about the experiences of others and without much concern for the impact their words and actions have on others.

Multicultural competence is not about achieving a title that can be displayed on a résumé or business card. Nor is it about achieving a certain requisite amount of knowledge or having accomplished a certain amount of social justice deeds. In fact, I believe that the intentional decision to embark upon the journey is far more significant than whether or not you have arrived at a certain destination. If someone asks, "Are you a multiculturally competent professional?" you can answer, "I'm trying to be. I'm working on it. I'm committed to being more multiculturally competent every day." If you can honestly say that you are on the road, then I would consider you a multiculturally competent helping professional.

I encourage you to embrace the realistic goal of competence rather than expertise. You do not need to be an expert on cultural history and experiences to embrace continued growth. The following worksheet will help you further explore your own multicultural competence journey.

Cultural Competency Journey Reflection

In what ways am I on the road to cultural competence?

_____

_____

_____

In what ways am I on the sidelines?

_____

_____

_____

What opportunities do I have to learn more or do more to move farther along the road?

_____

_____

_____

How can I encourage others to join me on the road and increase their cultural competence?

_____

_____

_____

Acculturation: There's More Than One Healthy Way

Acculturation has been defined as (1) the extent to which an individual or family retains selected aspects of their heritage culture and (2) the extent to which an individual or family pursues relations with members of their receiving culture (Berry, 1980). This definition applies whether a family comes to the United States from another country or whether a family moves from one part of this country to another part of this country. Acculturation describes how well an individual or family adjusts to that transition experience. There are four common acculturation experiences that are beneficial to be aware of: separated, assimilated, marginalized, and integrated.

Separated

Consider a large city, such as Chicago, where you can be driving down a main street that looks like all the rest, but after crossing a certain stop light, everything looks different. For example, you might notice that all of the signs are in Chinese. That's because you have entered the area of town referred to as Chinatown. There you will find restaurants that specialize in Chinese food and retail stores displaying artifacts from Chinese culture. The language around you will be Chinese, and even the street signs and décor will reflect Chinese culture. Many of the individuals who consider this community their home can be considered *separated*. Even though they are in Chicago, a large city in the United States, there is value for and an intentional effort to maintain aspects of their first culture.

Assimilated

Consider a married couple who bring their children to the United States from Mexico in order to give their children a chance at a better life. With sincere motivations, they leave their family customs behind and make every effort to integrate themselves into American culture. They learn English and change their clothes, customs, and ways of being, all in an effort to "learn how to be American." They actively pursue relationships with members of their host culture at the expense of their first culture. We can consider this family to be *assimilated*.

Marginalized

Consider a family who leaves their home country due to civil unrest. With assistance from a refugee program, they settle in America, only to find their hopes of feeling culturally at home in their new environment unfulfilled. Because they left their country with little more than the clothes on their backs and were unable to bring many artifacts reflecting their cultural heritage with them, they make intentional efforts to preserve their original language in their home. However, they make genuine efforts to fit into American society by learning to speak, dress, and spend their time like Americans, as well as to value what Americans value. Despite these efforts, they don't feel accepted in their immediate environment. Without feeling connected to their home country, and without successful transition to this new country, they feel *marginalized*.

Integrated

Consider a family who comes to America from another country and who also brings with them as much as they feel reasonably necessary to preserve key aspects of their cultural heritage while also leaving room for new values, customs, and ways of being. In turn, they feel more comfortable in their new country and feel accepted and welcomed. At home, they may speak one or both languages, even though outside of the home they speak primarily English, and they don't feel conflicted by such. They don't sacrifice one cultural expression or value for the sake of the other. Effort is made to delicately balance or *integrate* both cultures into their daily lives and interactions.

Identifying Healthy Acculturation

There are many who conclude that *integrated* is the type of acculturation every individual or family should strive for. However, there are others who suggest that there can be a healthy manifestation of all four.

For example, let's return to the *separated* residents and business owners of the Chinatown area in Chicago. Some outsiders believe that these Chinatown occupants prefer to live an exclusive life, isolating themselves from the American culture outside of their walls and preferring that visitors stay away. These outsiders might be surprised to hear that many Chinatown residents welcome visitors into their stores and restaurants. It gives the residents an opportunity to spread awareness and appreciation for the culture they value so much and allows them to shatter negative stereotypes. In addition, some might find it surprising to learn that these Chinatown residents voluntarily leave the area on a regular basis to conduct necessary business and to experience and learn about the customs and ways of America. The reason they return to Chinatown after these experiences is because they value their cultural heritage so much that they want to preserve and maintain it—and this is just one of many ways to do so. They may be separated, but it is voluntary and without significant internal or interactional detriment.

Similarly, consider the *assimilated* parents who brought their children to the United States from Mexico to give them a better life. Imagine that they are in family therapy and the therapist concludes that the cause of their relationship struggles is their effort to assimilate to American culture. Upon hearing this theory, the parents express to the therapist, "I'm not sure what movies you've have been watching, but the culture we left behind was not a glamorous fiesta. We left an environment that was riddled with drugs and crime, where law enforcement and politicians were just as corrupt as the drug dealers and other criminals." For this family, *assimilation* could be a healthy acculturation goal that is best for them.

Now let's assume that this same therapist also happens to be working with the *marginalized* family who left their home country due to civil unrest. When the therapist shares the same theory with the marginalized family—conveying the belief that the family's marginalized status is the cause of their struggles—the family responds by saying, "I'm not sure what refugee movie you've been watching, but we didn't come to America because we heard this country was the greatest thing since sliced bread. America wasn't our dream. It was just a safer place and where the rescue plane happened to land. As a matter of fact, in our country of origin, *family* is what is most central to our sense of culture, not identification with our country. As long as our family is intact, then while we may be marginalized, we are not conflicted by a longing for either side. Our family is the core of our cultural identity, wherever we may be." For this family, being *marginalized* could be a healthy acculturation goal that is best for them.

Finally, *integration* usually needs little explanation as a healthy acculturation goal, given that this balance makes sense for many people and fits acculturation expectations. However, as these examples have reflected, we should make intentional efforts to accept various forms of healthy acculturation, even if it doesn't fit our expectations. This is especially the case if it doesn't fit what we would be comfortable with if we were in a similar situation.

As a therapist, I am reminded of one of the guiding principles of the DSM-5, which suggests that you can meet all the symptom criteria for a particular disorder, but if those symptoms are not impairing your functioning in daily life, then you do not meet criteria for that disorder. Similarly, an individual or family can be in a separated, assimilated, or marginalized acculturation state, but if they are not distressed by their situation, then I encourage you to accept their acculturation choice without feeling the need to fix what isn't broken.

Acculturation Across Family Members

Acculturation is also known to vary across family members, including between parents and children. Consider a Korean couple who are grateful for the opportunity to raise their first-generation children in America and who are, at the same time, frustrated with the behavioral and attitudinal choices their adolescent children are making, which seem to reflect undesirable influences of certain aspects of American culture.

When the parents initiate family therapy, they state, "We need help with our children. We wanted them to grow up in America so they could have more opportunities than we had. We knew there would be some aspects of American culture that they would pick up, and we were and are okay with that. We like how well they are adjusting, the things they are learning, and how we are even learning some things through their experiences. However, there are some things they do, some ways in which they speak, and some new values they have that we are not comfortable with. And when we try to talk about it, they don't obey us. We're not trying to control them; we are just concerned that they are picking up everything—the good and the bad—and we need your help in protecting our children from their risky behavior."

Upon hearing this genuine expression of concern, the adolescents turn to their parents and say, "Well you never said it like *that*. You never said that you liked how well we were adjusting, learning, and growing up. It feels like you're always complaining that we're just doing everything everyone else does and leaving our cultural ways of being behind. In actuality, we value our culture's values and ways of life more than you think. We don't want to do everything our friends do because of the values we have. There are even times when we go over our friends' houses and see how they talk to one another and interact, and we're grateful for our family. We don't like all aspects of either culture, but we're teens. We're still figuring it all out."

The parents respond, "Well *you* never said *that*! All you ever say to us is how much we are overreacting and how we should just let you make your own decisions. If you would have let us know that you share some of our cultural values and are intentionally making efforts to preserve them, then it might be easier to trust you both and to engage in more meaningful discussion, rather than just fighting for the right to enforce behaviors."

This dialogue reflects how acculturation isn't always experienced the same by all individuals in a family. This doesn't necessarily have to be a problem. The question is "How much awareness is there of the impact of acculturation on someone's words, actions, and emotions?" It's not about choosing which culture is best pursued. **It's about how one wrestles with and determines the role that their cultural background will play in their current cultural environment.**

Colorblindness

Many conversations involving acculturation include the use of a common term: *colorblind*. When encountering an individual from an ethnic minority background, some offer this positive and reassuring statement: "When I look at you, I don't see color." Unfortunately, these same individuals have difficulty understanding that this well-intentioned expression isn't always experienced as reassuringly as it was intended.

If the expression conveys, "When I look at you, I don't let the color of your skin or differences in our ethnic heritage stop me from treating you with value and respect," then it may very well be received with appreciation. However, if it conveys, "When I look at you, I act as if our ethnic cultural backgrounds and experiences don't matter because we're all the same," then the response might be "I'd appreciate it if you wouldn't think that way." If someone's ethnic cultural heritage is an important aspect of their identity, then for them, if you don't see color, you don't truly see them.

Melting Pot

Many conversations about acculturation also lead to the depiction of America as a great *melting pot*. This idea often conveys a mental picture of America that is composed of various individuals and families from around the world, different in many ways but nonetheless all a part of the same big melting pot.

Many people experience America similarly to that of the slightly overcooked soup, such that "people from all over the world are welcome, as long as they learn how to be American"—even though the exact definition of what that means varies widely.

THE OVERCOOKED SOUP

Consider... a large pot, where there is vegetable soup steaming. The soup includes carrots, celery, tomatoes, onions, bell peppers, and squash, all in a flavorful broth. Now consider what would happen if this soup was over a fire for a bit too long and became slightly overcooked. If you had some of the soup, you'd still be able to enjoy a nice-tasting, flavorful dish. However, if you bit into the individual ingredients of the soup, you'd soon realize that while there was great variety in the soup's ingredients, they ultimately lost their uniqueness and took on the overall flavor of the soup.

Salad Bowl

Acknowledging the benefits, as well as the limitations, of the melting pot metaphor, there has been an effort in some academic circles to find an alternative metaphor that can maintain the advantages of the melting pot while reducing its disadvantages. As a result, the melting pot has been replaced with the *salad bowl*.

APPRECIATING UNIQUE INGREDIENTS

Consider... a large bowl containing a fresh garden salad. The salad comprises green leaf lettuce, thin slices of cucumber, shredded carrots, chopped boiled egg crumbles, and cherry tomatoes, with a light sprinkle of shredded cheese. When taking a bite of this salad, you get a burst of fresh ripe tomato on one side of your mouth, alongside a crunch of carrot on the other side. The more you chew, the more you experience not only the great-tasting flavor of this salad as a whole, but also the unique textures and flavors of each ingredient.

While the melting pot requires a sacrifice of uniqueness, the salad bowl celebrates this uniqueness. The use of the salad bowl metaphor discourages assimilation that requires people to sacrifice their uniqueness at the door, and it instead appreciates variety in culturally diverse experiences. We can encourage common experiences alongside unique contributions and recognize that uniqueness enhances growth in communities. Use the worksheet on the next page to reflect on your own experience in witnessing other people's cultural values and customs, including how you can demonstrate interest in the unique experiences that others have to share.

Cultural Competency Journey Reflection

What values and customs would I want to maintain even if I relocated to another country where the values and customs differed?

_____

_____

_____

What cultural values and customs do I see around me that differ from the norm but that people may be preserving based on a genuine motivation?

_____

_____

_____

What opportunities do I have to learn more about the motivation behind certain cultural values with which I am not familiar?

_____

_____

_____

How can I show genuine interest and appreciation for unique and varied values and cultural expressions?

_____

_____

_____

A Client-Centered Approach to Cultural Competence

Now that we have addressed some foundational concepts regarding multicultural awareness and competence, I would like to discuss how to put that increased awareness and competence into practice a little more directly. I believe that one of the most practical ways to accomplish this is to borrow from the person-centered approach originated by psychologist Carl Rogers (1959), who promoted three core conditions that, if employed effectively, can help create the relational safe space needed to bring about positive change: empathy, unconditional positive regard, and genuineness. While these core conditions are often used by mental health professionals as a core theoretical orientation, they can also be useful as practical strategies for building and maintaining rapport. The beauty of these principles is that they can be done one relationship at a time.

Empathy

Empathy is the action of putting yourself in someone else's shoes or seeing things from someone else's perspective. One of the goals of empathy is to be able to validate another person's perspective and feelings as legitimate based on that person's personal history and cultural experiences. It is *not* the same thing as approving of these experiences as "right" or "wrong."

One practical way to accomplish empathy is to make intentional efforts to relate to others based on your closest personal or professional experiences—and to accept the similarities, as well as the limitations, of your experiences. When you can relate to another person's situation in any way, it makes it easier to convey genuine understanding and value for their perspective. Interestingly, you don't need to have shared the same experience in order to empathize. You only need to find at least one thing to connect with—such as a similar experience of loss, hurt, and so forth—and that one thing can then become the relatable foundation for your increased understanding of the experiences you don't share. You don't need to *completely* understand; you need to understand *enough* to empathize.

Empathize with Everyone

Although admittedly it is not an easy endeavor, I encourage you to join me on a personal challenge to pursue empathy with anybody, anywhere, on any topic. The goal is neither about agreement nor approval. It is about taking the time to explore *why* a person feels so strongly about something and understanding the experiences that contributed to their conclusion or feelings. It is pointless to try to argue or debate feelings away because feelings don't work that way. Two people can see the same facts, draw similar conclusions about the implications of those facts, and still feel differently about it in the end. Instead of arguing about feelings, it can be a very powerful relational moment for one person to say to another, "I can see why you feel so strongly about what you believe. I still have reasons and my own experiences that lead me to feel differently, but that doesn't stop me from hearing and validating your perspective as legitimate."

Empathy Keeps the Focus on Genuine People

Making the effort to empathize has multiple benefits. One benefit is that it helps you remember that you are speaking to and seeking to help a person who has their own feelings and unique perspectives, as well as past, present, and future experiences of value. This is in contrast to falling into the trap of arguing a faceless point or solving a faceless problem. Too often it can be easy to discount or devalue a person, their experiences, and their perspective simply because they believe or feel differently. Empathy encourages value for the person and their perspectives, which you may not share but can still choose to respect.

Empathy Softens Oppositional Responses

Another benefit of empathy is that it can soften an oppositional response and open someone else's ears to hear your perspective more effectively in return. To put it simply, if you respect others in their differences, they are more likely to feel compelled to respect you in your differences.

No One Is "Unempathizable"

One of the most common difficulties in empathizing with another is the belief that some people are so different that we couldn't possibly empathize or understand that person's perspective. This is where I remind you of the diversity wheel and the revelation that while we can very well have significant differences between us, there are still likely some similarities that can be found.

If you make an intentional effort to put a spotlight on those similarities, then there is the potential to make the perceived "unempathizable" gap seem less insurmountable. Sure, you may be from a different cultural background, have a different gender or sexual orientation, or adhere to different faith beliefs. However, you may live in a similar region, work in the same career field, and share similar family values. Taking the time and energy to look for similarities and using them to help you understand others can plant seeds of hope and mutual understanding.

Unconditional Positive Regard

Contrary to popular belief, unconditional positive regard does not involve being happy about everything. It involves providing acceptance, support, and respect for another person just as they are. This can look like taking a positive and healthy interest in someone else's experiences rather than being inconvenienced by their differences. Too often, people from various cultural minority groups experience their minority status as something that makes other people feel uncomfortable or inconvenienced, which often impacts their experiences in negative ways. As a result, these individuals find themselves going out of their way to suppress or compensate for their differences. How much of a relief would it be to encounter a helping professional who is not inconvenienced by cultural differences? Someone who takes a genuine interest in those differences by seeking to learn, understand, and value them? When people experience unconditional positive regard, they are relieved of the burden of feeling the need to suppress or explain away their cultural uniqueness.

WHAT'S IN A NAME?

Consider... an individual from an ethnic minority background, whose name happens to reflect his cultural heritage, and who is meeting a therapist for the first time. The therapist looks at the name printed on the intake form, struggles outwardly with how to pronounce it correctly, then after a few seconds of stumbling through unsuccessfully, gives up and asks, "Is it okay if I just call you Bob?"

On the one hand, the client in this situation may sincerely prefer to go by an acceptable nickname rather than to have the helping professional horribly mangle his real name repeatedly. On the other hand, he may not appreciate the professional's decision to call him by a made-up name rather than his real name. That being said, the dilemma still remains since it also isn't reasonable to expect professionals to perfectly pronounce a name that originates in a culture they are not familiar with on the first try.

So how can unconditional positive regard help address this dilemma? By exhibiting an air of respect and curiosity—rather than one of inconvenience—the helping professional can recognize and openly acknowledge their difficulty as soon as possible. With confident humility, the professional could then say, "You know, this is a very unique name—at least in my experience. And you've probably heard it mispronounced by people before. Can you take a moment to help me understand the correct pronunciation so I can address you correctly moving forward?"

Even though this requires a little more work on the client's behalf, it shows that the helping professional values the client enough as a person to ask this question. This has the potential to earn the helping professional significant respect at the very beginning of the relationship. Even if they are unable to pronounce the name perfectly, their attempt to pronounce it can have a positive impact because it can be viewed as a genuine effort, rather than a disrespectful lack of positive regard or a failure to try in the first place.

THE QUINCEAÑERA

Consider... a female therapist waiting for a family who is late for their therapy session. When the family arrives, they immediately apologize for their tardiness, explaining that the reason for their delay was because their daughter's recently concluded Quinceañera went a little over time. They reassure the therapist that they did their best to depart the festivities as soon as reasonably possible because they didn't want to miss the family therapy session.

The therapist politely and professionally responds by saying, "Thank you for letting me know why you were late. Unfortunately, if you truly valued your family therapy sessions, you would have made more of an intentional effort to arrive on time because we only have a limited amount of session time, and in order for it to be most effective, there needs to be consistency. Let's talk more about your priorities as a family and what changes you can make so your actions line up with your expressed values."

This unfortunate scenario reflects a missed opportunity on the part of the therapist. On the one hand, there is a significant benefit to promptness, consistency, and priority within the therapeutic process. These factors are known to contribute to long-lasting and positive outcomes. On the other hand, the fact that this family cut short a very significant cultural family event in order to maintain that consistency seems more evident of the priority they place on therapy. Instead of critiquing this family's tardiness, this therapist could have taken a few minutes to take a healthy interest in this cultural event given its importance to the family: "Thanks for the apology and the consideration for the value of our time together. If you don't mind my asking, isn't the Quinceañera the coming of age ceremony for Hispanic young women at the age of 15? Can you tell me a little more about it, how it went, and what it means to you?"

By asking these questions, the therapist acknowledges her ignorance, asks for new information, and shows that she has some knowledge of the family's culture, which she can build upon rather than making the family responsible for teaching her everything. In addition, it shows that the therapist places value on what is important to the family without taking away from the therapist's own values. The conversation then becomes therapeutic because it is an opportunity for the therapist to learn more about the family's values that underlie their therapeutic goals—which is what influenced them to initiate therapy in the first place. This gesture of unconditional positive regard helps the clients feel seen and valued from a cultural perspective, which can strengthen the therapeutic relationship and increase the family's comfort with the therapist.

Genuineness

Finally, Rogers's third component of therapeutic change is genuineness, which involves being your open and honest self. When you are genuine, you express your thoughts and feelings without putting up a professional façade in front of the client. It is personally and professionally beneficial to learn how to accept your authentic self, which you can explore through increasing your cultural self-awareness. Genuineness conveys a sense of stability and has the potential to increase your client's comfort level with you. Additionally, when you exhibit genuineness, it models to clients what balance looks like and encourages them to feel safe enough to express their genuine self with you. In a world where many people don't feel safe expressing vulnerability, especially when cultural differences may potentially be perceived as barriers, cultivating genuineness can encourage others to risk sharing themselves and can give you a chance to show them you support them despite those differences.

THE NEW CLIENT

Consider... a seasoned therapist who accepts a referral from a trusted colleague. Despite this therapist's many years of service, this would be his first client from a Hispanic background. Recognizing feelings of uncertainty alongside a sincere desire to make the new client feel comfortable, the therapist decides to take down several random decorative trinkets and replace them with sombreros and other stereotypically Hispanic items. The therapist then removes the soft elevator music in the waiting room and replaces it with mariachi music. Still feeling like he hasn't done enough, the therapist greets the new client upon arrival with a big handshake and a boisterous "Buenos días!"—to which the client responds with a confused look and a cautious handshake, saying, "I speak English. Do you?" and thinking, *What's going on here? I hope I didn't make the wrong decision.*

What went wrong in this scenario was not a lack of sincere intentions. Rather, the therapist was trying to be something he wasn't. It wasn't genuine. It wasn't authentic. I suggest we pursue a more realistic goal. It is impossible to change who we are for everyone we seek to help. Instead, the more we understand about the many characteristics within us that contribute to who we are, the more variety of our true selves we can share.

You don't have to have lived through every cultural experience in order to help someone feel comfortable. In fact, trying to do so has the potential to decrease your professional credibility. You don't go into a physician's or lawyer's office and expect them to change their office around because you walked in. You expect them to be their genuine selves and to show that they accept your authentic self, learn more about you over time, and provide the professional service you are there to receive.

Despite sincere efforts, "trying too hard" can have detrimental effects on healthy relationship building. But remember, this isn't about judging yourself for making mistakes; in fact, it's the opposite. If you accept that differences are okay, that missteps will happen, and that unintended offenses will occur, then you can focus your efforts instead on cultivating empathy, unconditional positive regard, and genuineness. These relationship-building strategies can lay a foundation for healthy cultural learning and interaction.

Self-Disclosure: To Share or Not to Share

When professionals work to enhance their empathy skills, the question often arises as to whether or not they should share their own experiences or keep them to themselves. To make self-disclosure simple, I will acknowledge that there are pros and cons to self-disclosure in your professional helping efforts.

One advantage of self-disclosure is that when you share your experiences with your client, it can enhance your understanding of the other person's internal experiences. Sharing those experiences can result in your client feeling less alone and more understood. However, a disadvantage of self-disclosure is that any perceived differences between your experiences and that of your clients could be perceived as more of a barrier than a similarity, effectively reducing chances at rapport and therapeutic effectiveness.

CLOSE, BUT NOT CLOSE ENOUGH

Consider... a therapist who is actively listening to her client express the difficulties he has had coping. As she listens, the therapist identifies four ways in which her experiences have been similar to the client's. After the client finishes expressing his feelings, the therapist reflects back what she heard and then chooses to connect with this client by self-disclosing how her experiences have been similar, hoping to help the client feel more understood and less alone.

In response, the client says, "Thanks for being willing to be vulnerable and share about yourself. And yes, it is a pleasant surprise to hear that our experiences have been similar in three out of the four ways that you described. Unfortunately, that fourth example doesn't seem so similar to me, and since that is the most important factor in my experience and not one of the things we share, then it is clear to me that you won't be able to fully understand what I need you to understand. So thanks for trying, but I'll go ahead and see myself out."

In this scenario, it wasn't wrong for the therapist to identify similarities between her experiences and the client's experiences. While it's possible that sharing the similarity in her experiences could have its intended positive impact, the benefits of sharing those experiences must be weighed against the risks of doing so—namely, potential damage to the relationship.

Admittedly, it can feel paralyzing to acknowledge the pros and cons of self-disclosure without having a clear plan for which to value most. Therefore, I offer this consideration: **You can get most of the benefits of self-disclosure without actually self-disclosing**. Consider this same therapist. Instead of identifying her shared experiences, she could have instead expressed, "*Some* people who experience what you're going through feel _____. Is that close to what you are feeling?" or "*Some* people who have gone through similar experiences struggle and wrestle with _____. Is that something you struggle with as well?" The aforementioned "*some* people" could be referring to the therapist, a previous client, or someone the therapist heard of directly or indirectly.

The point need not be that the therapist personally experienced these similarities. Rather, the point is that the therapist cared to listen and understand enough to explore and identify potential similarities. That way, if the client agrees with the comparisons, he and the therapist can move on from it accordingly with a stronger connection and increased rapport. And if the client disagrees with a particular comparison, he can feel free to reject the unidentified person's experience (rather than rejecting the therapist) and share why he feels his experience is different. The client and therapist can then move on from the discussion with clarified understanding.

There may be some helping professionals reading this who, whether based on their preferred professional strategy or simply their natural personality type, feel compelled to share their personal stories and experiences as a strategy for connecting with others. I encourage you to be very intentional and selective about your self-disclosure. Make sure you are selectively choosing what to share based on the needs of the client.

In your efforts to increase your skills as a culturally competent helping professional, I also encourage you to continually look for similarities and differences between yourself and those you are supporting and to practice sharing in a way that keeps the focus on your understanding of your client and their experiences. And always be aware of the impact of self-disclosure on your client's current needs and future goals. Use the worksheet on the next page to reflect on how you can better create a safe relational space with these goals in mind.

Cultural Competency Journey Reflection

Are there individuals or groups of people I have a particularly difficult time empathizing with? If so, what experiences contributed to this difficulty?

_____

_____

_____

_____

In what ways can I improve in my expression of unconditional positive regard for others?

_____

_____

_____

_____

Do I feel more inclined to self-disclose too much or too little? How can I become more intentional in my self-disclosure?

_____

_____

_____

_____

A Reasonable Professional Responsibility

Many of the considerations addressed so far have served to lay a foundational understanding that can help reduce the occurrence of cultural offenses. However, no matter how much effort you invest in reducing microaggressions, we must accept the inevitability of offense. After all, even without malice, disrespect, or callous disregard, ignorance will always be present to some degree, and this alone can lead to unintentional cultural offenses. In light of such, let's address some practical strategies for addressing microaggressions and other cultural offenses when they inevitably occur:

Regularly look for abrupt changes in rapport. As a helping professional, it is your responsibility to watch for potential signs of offense. This is less about mind reading and more about acknowledging that while it would be very convenient for the person who feels offended to be the one responsible for sharing those feelings, they might have reason to believe you won't hear or receive their feelings. Therefore, look for external signs of a loss of connection to show that you are receptive to cultural sensitivities. Some signs of offense include the following:

- **Resistance:** If you are in a working relationship with someone who was previously receptive to you but suddenly begins to push back, and you can find no clear reason in the content of your interactions, it's possible that they perceived something differently than how you intended, causing that person to feel the need to protect themselves.

- **Non-Compliance:** If you are collaborating with someone in order to provide helpful guidance and they suddenly become less cooperative, it's possible that a cultural offense decreased their willingness to invest in the relationship.

- **Withdrawal:** If you are helping someone who seemed emotionally invested in receiving your help and who was doing whatever was within their power to change, and suddenly they seem to have emotionally withdrawn, then you may have committed a cultural offense.

- **Early Termination:** If you find yourself having been canceled on multiple times, or a client ceases treatment without the courtesy of an explanation, one possibility is that an unintended cultural offense may have done damage to the professional rapport.

Regularly looking for abrupt changes in rapport doesn't mean you'll always see them. However, if you're looking for them, you're more likely to see them when they occur. It reminds me of the *Baader-Meinhof* phenomenon, also known as the frequency illusion, where something that is brought to your attention in a new way suddenly increases your awareness of that thing. It's like when you're looking to buy a new car and you find a car you've never seen before—and then all of a sudden you see that car multiple times a week. It's not because that car is new to the streets but because it's new to your awareness. The goal is not to make every threat to professional rapport a cultural issue but to keep your eyes open for potential cultural misunderstandings that may need repair. And if you see evidence of a cultural offense, hopefully you will be compelled to try to repair the relationship and reduce the likelihood of a repeat occurrence.

Own the impact of the microaggression. If your awareness is increased and you see an abrupt change in the relationship—and you've built up enough rapport that the client doesn't immediately withdraw—then another practical and impactful step you can take is to own the impact of the microaggression. I am not suggesting that it is always necessary or even appropriate to own the microaggression itself. Rather, owning the *impact* of the microaggression focuses more on acknowledging that our words or actions can be experienced as offensive to someone else. **Don't waste time defending yourself against accusations that are based on experiences that precede you**. Without misplaced shame or guilt, you can own the impact rather than the cause of the hurt: "I noticed what seemed like a change in your body language, and all of a sudden it seems as though the conversation between us is less comfortable. If you don't mind my asking, did I say or do anything that made you feel uncomfortable? If so, it's important to me that you know it was not my intent, and I want to do whatever I can to clear up any misunderstandings and move forward together."

This type of response acknowledges your awareness and overt openness to owning the impact of your actions, and it transitions to the third step in addressing microaggressions: initiating healing.

Initiate healing to the relationship. It is your responsibility as a helping professional to initiate healing of the therapeutic relationship by addressing the damage that resulted from the microaggression. You must take the initiative not because of fault, consequent guilt, or shame but because of the opportunity it provides you to rebuild trust and repair the relationship. You can accomplish this by cultivating skills such as flexibility, respect, curiosity, and unconditional positive regard—all of which have the potential to convey an openness to learning about clients' values and comfort zones. It lets the client know that you want to help them achieve what they are hoping for in their lives, rather than oppressing them with your values and preferences for their lives based on what is comfortable for you.

One more thing about responsibility. While I stand by the notion that the helping professional is responsible for initiating these relationship-repair strategies, this is not intended to enable or create a victim mentality for the client. Rather, it is intended to support optimal learning for the client. As you take the lead in recognizing the change in rapport, owning the impact of the offense, and initiating healing, these behaviors indirectly provide a healthy model the client can use to address perceived microaggressions outside of the professional relationship. If after this experience, the client inadvertently offends another, instead of reacting by defending themselves and focusing on avoiding blame, it's possible they might pause and think to themselves, *This looks familiar. It looks a lot like how I responded to feeling offended. I wonder what it would look like if I tried repair and understanding.* It's very possible that the efforts you employ to repair, salvage, and even strengthen the therapeutic relationship can indirectly teach clients how to repair and strengthen their relationships.

Use the reflection worksheet on the next page to explore how you can address microaggressions and other culture offenses when working with clients. Then use the cultural self-assessment tool to explore how cultural differences or past experiences may influence your current views.

Cultural Competency Journey Reflection

What habits can I build to remind me to intentionally look for abrupt changes in rapport that might be reactions to unintended cultural offenses?

_____

_____

_____

What would it sound like for me to own the impact of a potential microaggression?

_____

_____

_____

How might I initiate healing to a relationship where there has been unintentional damage due to a cultural misunderstanding?

_____

_____

_____

What difficult past experiences might make it more difficult for me to work with certain types of clients? Which clients are those?

_____

_____

_____

Identifying Multicultural Perspectives

Helping professionals, no matter how self-aware, are not immune to the influence of past experiences on their current interactions with others. Therefore, it is important to take efforts to identify and explore how your past experiences inform your current interactions, including how they may contribute to any perceived cultural offenses that occur. Doing so will help you respond in healthier ways and will allow you to gain a better understanding of the growth process that you are challenging your clients to voluntarily engage in as well.

Take a moment to explore the ways in which your past personal and professional experiences may influence your views, perspectives, and interactions with individuals from various cultural backgrounds.

Are there any individuals from particular cultural backgrounds who make me feel angry, resentful, anxious, or uncomfortable (even before I interact with them)?

_____

_____

_____

_____

What past experiences have I had that may be contributing to these feelings?

_____

_____

_____

_____

What are the legitimate reasons for my feelings?

_____

_____

_____

_____

In what ways can I change my perspective in light of my increasing cultural empathy and understanding of people from various backgrounds?

_____

_____

_____

_____

Addressing Transference

Transference occurs when an individual directs their feelings toward one person while the origins of those feelings are based on experiences involving someone else, which is very similar to many microaggression responses. And while there are many reasons transference can occur, oftentimes an aggressive response to a perceived offense is less reflective of the universal offensiveness of the word or action and more reflective of that person's past experiences. In light of such, it seems prudent to review common professional strategies to address transference. Here are a few practical skills to cultivate so you can be prepared to utilize them after offenses occur:

- **Reflect:** When you use reflection, you show the person you understand their words and feelings. It begins with listening well and selectively choosing which words to repeat back to them to convey that you heard and understood them. You can enhance this reflection by including your interpretations of what the client implicitly expressed. When it comes to reflection, it is often beneficial to intentionally avoid stating or implying that you *completely* understand the client's experience. Doing so would convey an absolute level of understanding that almost compels clients to defensively reply, "You can't possibly *completely* understand my experience unless you have gone through my exact experience." Instead, you can express that you understand enough "to see that..." and finish the sentence with the understanding you have gained.

- **Relate:** One of the best ways to support someone is to help them feel less alone, and relating can help you accomplish that. You can relate to the client by highlighting that despite your admittedly different experiences, you can intellectually or hypothetically understand the client's experience based on comparable feelings from your own past and current circumstances. Whether or not you utilize selective self-disclosure, relating can further show that you understand more than the client thinks you do, which builds a stronger connection and increases the effectiveness of your helping efforts.

- **Validate:** You don't have to agree with someone in order to validate the legitimacy of their feelings. It's not about whether their values and beliefs are right or wrong. It's about what they are feeling based on their past experiences. The goal is to be able to genuinely express, "In light of what you've experienced and learned from those experiences, I can see how you feel the way you do." This effort can also help you reduce the tendency to defend yourself if the client assertively or even aggressively expresses these feelings. The sooner we realize that our client's feelings—including their concerns, fears, and need for protection—likely preceded their interaction with us, the sooner we can begin to acknowledge the legitimacy of their feelings.

- **Empathize:** Empathizing with someone is not about feeling bad for someone else's predicament. It's taking the time to learn and understand what a person feels and why, and then showing that this exploration resulted in a genuine concern for their feelings. It also conveys that you care enough to help make their experience better, even if that means you may need to do somethings differently in your relationship with them to accomplish this goal.

- **Reassure:** Skills related to listening, understanding, and even caring have the potential to be passive endeavors that remain internal to us as helpers. In contrast, something powerful happens when these efforts are active, external gifts because it directly reassures our clients that we will make every effort to provide them with a healthier therapeutic experience. We can help our clients grow by being the healthy and safe learning environment they need to make significant life changes. If done well, you can even respond when a client is directly attacking you by welcoming the genuine expression of feeling as something the client legitimately needs to get out rather than bottle up. Show that you don't feel the need to judge or dismiss them for their feelings, and reassure them that you are still committed to helping them grow in whatever way possible.

Reflect. Relate. Validate. Empathize. Reassure. These are all practical skills you can learn and cultivate to increase authenticity and effectiveness. Identify which skills are not your strengths and begin to practice them. Identify which skills come naturally to you and cultivate them further. When used to address cultural fears, differences, barriers, and misunderstandings—and the damage these can cause to relationships—these skills have the potential to be the keys to genuine relationship repair.

Addressing Countertransference

Just as transference can occur when clients feel offended by something we do or say, we as helping professionals are not immune to feeling offended by our clients' words and actions. The goal is not to judge ourselves for being imperfect or for allowing our personal history, feelings, and perspectives to influence our helping efforts. We're imperfect humans as well. The goal is to acknowledge the inevitability of the impact of the past on the present, make efforts to reduce the negative impact, and increase the positive impact on present interactions and relationships. I will explore a few practical ways to accomplish this:

- **Look for it:** In order to address countertransference, we need to increase our self-awareness to know what it looks like in ourselves. I am not suggesting that we become preoccupied with looking for problems. Rather, I am noting that we're more likely to see countertransference when it occurs if we have self-awareness. For example, you might be experiencing countertransference if you (1) feel yourself getting unexpectedly or unjustifiably *angry* or *resentful* toward a client, (2) feel yourself getting *anxious* or *uncomfortable* with a client without sufficient experiences to account for those feelings, or (3) find yourself having *difficulty empathizing* with a client. It's possible that the reason you are struggling to find a sufficient current experience that fully accounts for your emotional struggles may be that there are past experiences influencing your perception of the present relationship. In order to address these struggles in a healthy manner, you need to first be willing to see them, to explore the possibility of their influence, and to have the self-esteem to do something about it.

- **Own it:** One thing you can do to address uncomfortable feelings about clients is to own the existence of the influence of the past on the present. Continually ask yourself whether cultural differences or past cultural experiences are positively or negatively influencing your current cultural perspective. This effort can help you own the good and the bad, the strengths and the growth areas, the helpful and the unhelpful—not as permanent traits but as contributing factors to who you are and what you do. You determine how much or how little these factors will play in your life. Owning it is also beneficial because it validates the other person's experience. Owning the impact of past experiences on your current responses conveys your desire to not make your clients responsible for your experience. This is much healthier than making someone else responsible for feeling the guilt and correcting the errors of those who came before them. Instead, mutually acknowledge the impact of the past on the present, and lay a foundation for working together to find solutions for the present and future alike.

- **Process it:** When you see potential barriers to healthy professional relationships, and you have sufficient self-esteem to own it, you can reduce the impact of these realities by processing and exploring them further. You can accomplish this by seeking professional help (e.g., from a mental health professional), consulting with a professional colleague, or expressing and exploring your thoughts and feelings privately through journaling. While these are just a few of the options available, and each have varying degrees of impact, the common benefit is that you are making an intentional effort to work through the barriers outside of your professional relationship so clients don't have to worry about your struggles hindering your ability to hear, understand, and help them grow.

Self-Disclosure of Countertransference

So far, when addressing countertransference, I have been referencing how to become aware of thoughts and feelings that may become *internal* barriers to genuine connection and empathy in the therapeutic relationship. However, the question naturally arises regarding what to do if that internal struggle becomes *external*, if those thoughts and feelings spill out into words and behaviors that convey your difficulties with empathizing and helping. For this dilemma, I present the following strategies:

Get ahead of your reactions. Increasing your self-awareness increases the likelihood that if countertransference struggles arise, you'll have a chance to see them internally before they spill out externally. If you feel something like this coming on, I strongly encourage you to get ahead of it and to keep it contained. Although it is not healthy to habitually bottle up feelings without proper processing, this is not what I am proposing. Rather, I am encouraging you to contain your feelings during relational interactions where it would not be appropriate to process them (e.g., when you're in a helping role with someone who is in a state of vulnerability). After the interaction, actively seek out an appropriate outlet to process those thoughts and feelings to reduce the likelihood that it will hinder your ability to see and serve others in a healthy manner.

Do not waste time beating yourself up for having past experiences that cause present difficulties. Own those feelings, process them, and reduce their negative impact—for your benefit, as well as the benefit of those seeking your support.

Be cautious about helpful self-disclosure. Some helping professionals believe it can be beneficial to self-disclose our countertransference with clients because it conveys that we are imperfect humans as well. To some degree this has merit, especially given that it is customary in some cultures to distrust anyone who is not willing to share the same degree of vulnerability. Nonetheless, it is also beneficial not to make that kind of self-disclosure completely transparent either. Put another way, be cautious about self-disclosing your countertransference with clients, as it may turn a professionally beneficial helping relationship into one where the client has to worry about your personal struggles and consequent ability to support them.

A PROFESSIONAL'S LOSS

Consider... a female therapist who is working with a male client to process the loss of his mother and its impact on how he is feeling and interacting at home and work. Unexpectedly, the therapist begins to visibly experience emotional distress. Through increasing tears, she expresses, "I'm sorry for my reaction. Don't worry; it reflects nothing bad about what you said. Rather, your situation reminds me of when I lost my mother, and while I thought that I had worked through it enough to not let it spill out in one of our sessions, it was such an unexpected..." Eventually, the therapist finishes self-disclosing, and the client, who was listening intently, passes the therapist a box of tissues and asks, "Is there anything else I can get for you?"

What went wrong here? To a certain extent, it is perfectly okay—and necessary—for therapists to have and acknowledge difficult experiences and resulting feelings. We are human after all. However, while we are operating in the role of a helping professional, we have a responsibility to manage our emotions on our own without shifting the responsibility over to the client. The goal here is not to push our feelings down, ignore them, or try to delete them altogether. Rather, we become skillful in seeing, owning, and processing our feelings on our own so our clients don't feel responsible for doing it for us.

An Acceptable Countertransference Self-Disclosure Exception

With the primary focus here being less about fear and more about intentional discretion regarding selective self-disclosure of countertransference, it is worth acknowledging and validating that, at times, it can be beneficial to self-disclose countertransference feelings. For example, using the previous example where the therapist lost her own mother, if the client returns to therapy the following week, the therapist can begin the session with:

> *"Welcome back. It's good to see you again. Before we pick up where we left off regarding progress on your goals, I wanted to address what occurred in our most recent session. I would like to apologize for letting my personal challenges spill over into the session. While it is reasonable for us all to have various struggles in life, it is also reasonable for you to expect me to use the precious and limited time that we have each week to focus on addressing and improving your circumstances, not mine. Therefore, I wanted to let you know that I will be increasing my efforts to process those issues on my own so our time can be most efficiently used as possible for your benefit."*

This professional self-disclosure is beneficial in multiple ways. First, it can reduce any discomfort between the therapist and the client so the experience doesn't become a taboo elephant in the room. Second, it can diminish the client's potential fear of needing to be cautious, less open, and more on guard with the therapist. In addition, if subsequent sessions do not repeat the same experience, it models for the client what healthy growth can look like. It gives the client the space to conclude, "If a helping professional can have, openly acknowledge, and work through their imperfections and life struggles, then maybe they can help me work through mine."

When Countertransference Becomes Too Much

Despite my belief that most individuals can address countertransference with personal or professional help, there may come a time when helping professionals are unable to overcome this barrier. If this occurs, I strongly recommend that you first consider this to be a temporary problem. It's not about *if* you can overcome this barrier but *how long* it will take you to overcome it. And if you ultimately conclude that it is in the client's best interest to seek help from a different professional, then it can be helpful for the client to know that this decision was based on your own struggles and does not reflect a value judgment of the client or their struggles.

A PROFESSIONAL'S LOSS—REVISITED

Consider... that same session where the client handed the therapist a box of tissues. Later that evening, as this client is contemplating what happened in session, he receives an unexpected call from the therapist's assistant, who explains that the therapist has determined that it would be in the client's best interest to transfer to a new therapist. The administrative assistant begins to explore available days and times when other therapists are available to reschedule. Unfortunately, the client respectfully declines and genuinely, yet reluctantly, says, "Why would I do that? My situation was so difficult to handle that I already broke one therapist. Why would I risk burdening someone else and breaking another therapist?"

In situations where you conclude that you are unable to sufficiently manage countertransference, it may benefit the client to directly hear the following sentiment from you: "It's not you, it's me." Although this phrase is very often frowned upon when it is used in the context of a romantic breakup, clients will likely appreciate hearing a direct, yet genuine, statement that conveys the need to refer them to another therapist better suited to meet their needs. This is not an option that you should take at the first sign of personal or professional discomfort since you can often process and work through countertransference without damaging the ongoing therapeutic relationship. I offer this recommendation for circumstances in which you have already attempted to manage countertransference without success.

For example, the therapist in the previous example could reach out and say:

"I wanted to reach out and address what occurred in our most recent session. I would like to apologize for letting my personal challenges spill over into the session. While it is reasonable for us all to have various struggles in life, it is also reasonable for you to expect me to use the precious and limited time we have each week to focus on addressing and improving your circumstances, not mine. Unfortunately, as I begin to explore the depth of my personal challenges, I am beginning to realize that it will take longer than would be ideal to make the progress I need to give you the undistracted help you deserve. Therefore, instead of leaving you to make progress on your own, I would like to refer you to one of my colleagues who I think would be a great fit for you. Additionally, if you wouldn't mind, I'd like you to give us permission to communicate briefly so I can

share as much as I can about what progress you have already made in therapy so you don't have to start at the beginning and you can pick up as closely as possible to where we left off."

A gesture like this has the potential to reinforce the genuine care that has permeated the helping relationship since the beginning. It also helps the client preserve a healthy view of their own struggles and gives them hope that with undistracted help, growth is still possible. This type of referral is also greatly appreciated by the next therapist because they have a chance to begin their helping efforts with fewer obstacles.

As you can see, self-disclosure has its advantages and its disadvantages, so it should not be taken lightly, nor should it be feared. I encourage you to begin to raise your personal antenna of self-awareness so if you find yourself with legitimate feelings arising from past cultural experiences, you'll have a better chance of seeing it, owning it, and processing it on your own so your clients won't have to.

Knowing *When* to Refer

In addition to issues regarding countertransference, there may be other situations when it is in the best interest of the client to seek services from a different professional. Let's explore strategies for when and how to appropriately refer someone to another professional service:

When clients have culture-specific needs that are beyond the scope of your practice. If there are cultural differences between you and your client, I consistently encourage you to avoid making the assumption that you cannot address the client's culture-specific needs due to those differences. Often, both you and your client can be pleasantly surprised by how much understanding, empathy, and support you can provide despite these cultural differences.

However, there are times when clients present with clearly defined goals specifically centered upon learning culture-specific history and knowledge. For example, a client might express at the first opportunity, "I'm here because I need to know about my specific cultural heritage so I can better learn the role it has in my life, and I need an expert who can guide me through this kind of cultural identification journey." In this case, if you feel like you do not have a sufficient amount of knowledge, it may be beneficial to refer this client to someone who is more knowledgeable. The recommendation to refer assumes that you have made efforts to increase your knowledge and that a referral is indeed in the best interest of the client.

When perceived differences become insurmountable barriers or a source of confrontation. There may also come a time when despite your best efforts to convey understanding, empathy, value, and respect, a client may perceive that the cultural differences in the therapeutic relationship are too much to overcome. In this case, clients may even feel the need to preemptively protect themselves from perceived judgment and oppression stemming from your helping efforts. If you recognize this dilemma and seek to repair the professional relationship by providing appropriate reassurance—but this proves insufficient—then it may be in the client's best interest to refer them to a therapist who might trigger less discomfort so you can increase the likelihood of a successful treatment outcome.

How to Refer

It can be disappointing to accept the reality that a referral may be necessary. However, it helps to remember that referrals are not a sign of failure. They are just another way to effectively help someone find the most appropriate care to meet their needs. It also helps to know that you are doing your best to refer in the most considerate way possible. To help you do so, here are a few strategies to facilitate referrals most effectively:

Avoid referrals based on discrimination, judgments, and cultural preferences. As previously discussed, everyone has personal and professional comfort zones. We all have people we're more comfortable with and people with we're less comfortable with. We need to personally acknowledge these preferences instead of judging them, and we need to make efforts to reduce the potential negative impact of these preferences on our helping efforts toward other people.

In circumstances where you have tried to help and conclude that it may be in your client's best interest to seek help elsewhere, take a moment to rule out the possibility that your conclusion isn't due to personal or professional discomfort on your part. If you explore your motivations and find yourself motivated by subtle judgments of your client's values, decisions, or behaviors, consider making this an opportunity to address your personal judgments rather than referring out the client who is the source of your discomfort. This is especially significant if your judgments are based on cultural ignorance and misunderstandings rather than legitimate differences that would be barriers to treatment. Personal preference and comfort zones can be so powerfully subtle that it can be easy to convince yourself that referring out clients for these reasons is justifiable because "Well, you know about people like that, right?"

Highlight the goal intended to benefit the client. In addition to reassuring clients that your decision to refer isn't based on judgment or discrimination, it is important to reassure them that the inconvenience is primarily to benefit them. As disappointing as it may be to need to be referred to someone new, it is reasonable for clients to want and expect to have a helping professional who feels competent.

Clearly communicating the motivation behind the need to refer is also beneficial because it helps avoid committing microaggressions. Many clients have experienced prior discrimination and judgments based on cultural differences and may be especially cautious about re-experiencing this. Unclear communication leaves room for misinterpretation and can do unnecessary damage to your professional relationship.

Build a network of appropriate referral sources. Referrals aren't absolute endorsements of the cultural beliefs or behaviors of every professional at another organization. Nor are referrals admissions of professional failure and cause for shame.

Referrals are an acknowledgment that despite every reasonable effort to meet a client's needs, more needs remain. And the best way to meet those needs is to point the client in the direction of someone who may be better equipped to meet those needs.

One of the difficulties with referrals is that helping professionals often conclude that they simply don't know of all the possible resources available to help their clients. Unfortunately, this conclusion is based on the expectation that professionals are only helpful if they instinctively know what their clients need most and where to find it. In contrast, I believe it is more reasonable for helping professionals to continually keep their eyes and ears open for other resources that address different areas of specialty. Helping professionals may think it's damaging to remind themselves of the needs they are not sufficiently equipped to meet. However, I believe this can strengthen their professional confidence because it also highlights the needs they *are* well equipped to meet.

I previously mentioned that it may be appropriate to refer a client to a more applicable service if the client has culture-specific needs that are beyond your scope of practice. If you make efforts to increase your scope of competence and still find that your client needs more than you can ethically provide, it can be beneficial to acknowledge the client's legitimate need and to express that although it's your sincere desire to help meet that need, doing so is beyond your limits. This provides your clients with a reasonable explanation that supports your recommendation that they seek help elsewhere. Rather than make this referral at random, you can narrow down a few choices for the client that seem like places to start. For example:

> "I have never worked at these services, but from what I read online (or learned when I made an exploratory call prior to this session), they seem to have services or programs that meet your needs better than I would be able to. Not only that, but they seem to have helping professionals with personal and professional experiences specifically in the areas where you seem to seek knowledge and understanding (e.g., the impact of a specific cultural history on current coping experiences or the internal struggles of individuals questioning their gender identity or sexual orientation). It is my hope that they will be able to provide direction beyond what I have been able to offer thus far."

The "narrow down their choices" strategy acknowledges that the goal is not to identify *the* perfect place. There are often too many factors that determine what service would be most helpful—many of which are outside your control (e.g., the rapport fit with the next professional, the accurate identification of needs, the other professional's ability to validate the client's cultural experiences). You can either suggest that the client find additional resources (and leave it them to find those resources on their own) or make these suggestions yourself and follow up by pointing the client in the direction of a few to start with. What's important is that the referral empowers the client to make that decision for themselves, while also appreciating your supportive gesture in this process.

Ethically Learning from Clients

As a helping professional, it is your responsibility to learn about your client. It is not your client's responsibility to teach you. The onus is on you to learn about your clients, whether it's from the interactions you have with clients themselves or from sources outside of the therapeutic relationship. If a client chooses to volunteer cultural information that helps you understand their cultural context, values, and potential influences, that's great, but it is a gift rather than an obligation.

When you're a helping professional, you don't have the luxury of saying, "Look, if it's important to the client, then I'll just assume they'll eventually tell me. If they don't tell me, or if I assume something inaccurate and they don't correct me, then it must have not been that important to them." You have the responsibility to take the lead by initiating certain conversations. You can even bring it up as a question: "If you don't mind my asking, is it possible *this* is important or *this* may be a factor?" If the client says no, it was still worth asking because not only did you rule out a potentially irrelevant line of reasoning and inquiry, but you also showed your desire to learn beyond what they specifically told you. And if the client says yes, you have gained rapport points for showing that you have taken what they gave you and used it to learn or deduce more. It demonstrates that you were able to help them understand more about their own experiences without having to become an expert on those unshared experiences yourself.

In addition, it is better to respectfully ask for clarification than to assume or be paralyzed by fear. Sometimes helping professionals believe that in order to truly be useful, they need to be perceived as all-wise or all-knowing. Realizing that they do not know everything, they fear that acknowledging their cultural ignorance will diminish their therapeutic authority and reduce their ability to help. Reassuringly, many clients acknowledge that it is unreasonable to expect professionals to know everything about them. Clients actually feel less respected if we pretend to have knowledge that we don't, and they feel more respected when they can see that we have a genuine desire to learn and understand their personal experiences.

At the same time, while it's okay to learn from your client, every effort must be made to avoid exploiting your client. Take care to avoid temporarily shifting the focus of the session such that you are no longer helping your client but using them as a source of potentially valuable information for personal gain. This might sound like "I always wanted to know about your culture. Can you tell me about it?" No matter how genuine the request may seem, it risks turning the session into a tutorial where the client is paying to teach you rather than being helped. Instead, the focus must remain on gaining a better understanding of the client's experiences for the sake of helping the client and ensuring consistency with the client's treatment goals.

In addition, remember that the client is the expert on their culture. Clients have varying expectations for the role of the helping professional—some more authoritarian, some more egalitarian. Regardless of your professional preference and what you hope to offer your client, **the client is still the best source of information on their personal experiences.** This doesn't mean that they are an expert on life but that they are the expert on themselves. This also doesn't mean that they know everything about themselves and that you have nothing to offer. Rather, you have the challenge of balancing your previous knowledge with the specific information you learned about them in session. If you make statements such as "Oh, don't worry. You don't have to say anything else. I know all about your culture. I read about you in chapter 6," there's a good chance it won't be well received.

When discrepancies or conflicting information arises, you need to remember that your client's experiences and perspective are the priority. In doing so, you convey to your client that your desire is, first and foremost, to learn about them, rather than to promote or perpetuate stereotypes learned elsewhere regarding people in this cultural group.

While it is considerate and respectful to avoid assuming too information about your client based on your perceived knowledge of their culture, there is a time and place for you to review potentially relevant information from outside sources and share that information with your client. **After all, just because you don't know everything doesn't mean you know nothing.** It is also a good idea to be careful when challenging your client on aspects of their culture based on potential discrepancies between what they say and what you previously understood. You may have learned from legitimate sources, but that doesn't mean that those things apply to everyone in the cultural group you learned about.

You can give them this gift by asking for clarification from a place of professional humility. This can be expressed as follows, "In order for you to not have the burden of feeling like you have to teach me from scratch, I want to share with you what I have learned and give you the opportunity to modify and personalize that information to reflect your experience." Another way to express professional openness could be, "It's my understanding that people from your cultural background have had this type of experience, which has resulted in feelings of oppression. Has that been your experience?"—again, openly welcoming their correction or modification where necessary.

The goal is to find a healthy balance between acknowledging what you know while also being flexible enough to give your client the freedom to personalize what you know to them, which actually helps you avoid falling into the trap of stereotypes and overgeneralizations. The client might feel free enough to respond to culturally balanced inquiries like these with "Actually, in many ways what you learned was right. Everyone in my family and even extended family experience that—except me. And that is just one of the ways in which I feel alone and lack familial support and need your help."

This is a direct invitation to value outside learning while also prioritizing the perspective and experience of the client we are helping in the moment. With practice, this is a skill that you can cultivate and convey with genuineness and sincerity.

Learning Outside of the Session

You can gain knowledge and perspective from a variety of sources. It is unreasonable to expect yourself to experience every possible life event in order to empathize with your clients. It is also unreasonable to discount the lessons learned from the experiences you have had because they are not identical to those of the clients you are trying to reach. However, if you consider your experiences to be limited, then it is beneficial to expand your perspective by learning from the experiences of others. To do so, you can learn from the experiences of professional colleagues, the experiences of past clients you have served, and the experiences of family and friends.

Media, in its various forms (e.g., television, movies, news), also has the potential to be a source of learning as it relates to the experiences of others. Unfortunately, many professionals denounce the validity of media portrayals. They claim that everyone knows the media's depictions of life are inevitably skewed and cannot be trusted. To a certain extent, these criticisms of the media have merit, as there is often a blurred line between accurately conveyed information and a skewed and sensationalized infotainment. At the same time, we must avoid the mistake of dismissing the validity of potentially eye-opening experiences based solely on the source. In practice, it is true that you shouldn't believe everything you hear in the media, but sometimes media exposure is the only exposure you'll ever have to learn about certain experiences. Therefore, rather than minimizing and dismissing media altogether, discernment is key. We must develop a habit of critically evaluating the validity of both personal and secondary experiences.

CINEMATIC INSPIRATION

Consider... a therapist who is working with a couple who is struggling with expressing and understanding each other's emotions. After the couples engages in several unsuccessful attempts at reflecting and paraphrasing, the therapist begins to lose hope. One partner expresses an emotion using words that remind the therapist of a romantic movie he's recently watched. In the movie, the same scenario played out that is currently playing out in the session. The therapist recalls the movie character's past experiences, present fears, and future hopes and says to one partner, "Can I ask you a question? Some people, when they express things similar to what you expressed, are using those words to convey x, y, and z. Is that related to what you are feeling and hoping would be understood?" The client's response is a resounding, "Yes!" The other partner then responds, "Well, that makes sense! Why didn't you say it that way in the first place?" At no point did the therapist ever say, "By the way, I was able to understand what you were saying because I watched a romantic movie last week," yet he was able to use media to enhance his understanding of the couple's dynamic in the session, even though he was not necessarily personally familiar with their struggles.

This unexpected revelation generated more sharing and more understanding, and it was all sparked by a lesson learned from a media portrayal of a fictional couple. In fact, it is possible that the inspiration for the storyline of that fictional couple was based on the writer's real relationship experience. And it's also possible that the fictional emotions the actors expressed onscreen were influenced by the their real relationship experiences. They took their own emotional revelations and their own personal experiences of joy, pain, jubilation, sorrow, extreme loss, and internal conflict, and they shared them with the rest of the world.

There are a variety of cultural experiences that we will never personally experience, but we don't have to share these experiences to learn from them. If we use discernment, we can intentionally expose ourselves to depictions of a wide variety of life experiences—those close and far, those encouraging and discouraging—and learn as much as we can about life outside of our own ethnocentric bubble. Then, when we see or hear things in our professional helping role that bring to mind those depictions, we can utilize them—not as sources of fact but as potential lines of inquiry and increased understanding. And all the while, we remember that the person we're interacting with is the determining factor for what is true for them in their lives.

Cultural Competency Begins Before Relationship Interactions Begin

As a marriage and family therapist, I'll admit that I often see the world through the lens of relationships. Therefore, in the process of learning to increase your cultural competency, it is beneficial to take some inspiration from a couple's journey to learn to cultivate intimacy.

TURN OFF THE LIGHTS

Consider... a husband who comes home after a long day at work. He opens the door to his home to see his wife washing dishes after feeding their children dinner. He gently kisses his wife on the cheek and hugs his children before heading upstairs to unpack and unwind from his long day.

After his wife finishes the dishes, and wipes off the stove and countertops, she straightens up the living room and begins the children's bedtime routine, which includes bath time, pajamas, brushing teeth, and a bedtime story.

When the children finally fall asleep, she walks upstairs to begin to unwind from her long day as well, and as she gets closer to the top of the stairs, she sees their bedroom door slightly ajar with dim lighting inside. When she reaches the door, she pushes it open to find red satin draped over the bedside lamp, creating a low red glow, and notices soft music playing in the background. Finally, her eyes rest on their bed, where she sees her husband looking at her, stretched out in a seductive pose.

Slightly confused, she asks, "What are you doing?"

He replies in an intentionally soft and seductive voice, "You know what I'm doing... You see the lights, you hear the music, you see 'the' boxers. I'm setting the mood."

In response, his wife says, "Oh, I see. You're setting the mood. Well, you know what would have set the mood? Starting the kids' bedtime routine while I was washing the dishes and cleaning up from today's chaos. That would have set the mood."

What went wrong? This well-meaning husband assumed that intimacy begins after crossing over the threshold of the bedroom door. However, for his wife, intimacy begins long before they enter the bedroom. Long before physical intimacy is even an option, there is the potential for emotional intimacy. Her husband's effort to take some of the bedtime routine off her shoulders would have done more to put her in a similarly intimate mindset than any environmental mood-setting effort.

Just as relationship intimacy begins before physical encounters, cultural competency development begins before actual cross-cultural interactions. Long before a therapy, coaching, or mentoring session occurs, you can make efforts to learn as much as possible about the experiences of others outside of yourself. It doesn't even have to be about a specific group of people but can involve learning—as often as possible—about as many types of people as possible, from as great a variety of sources as possible. That way, when you do have the opportunity to encounter someone from a different cultural background than yourself, you may not have to start from scratch in your effort to understand and relate to their experiences—even if it's because you saw something in a movie one time.

The worksheet on the next page can help you reflect on your own journey in learning about other cultural experiences and perspectives.

Cultural Competency Journey Reflection

What opportunities do I currently have to learn about others' experiences to relieve them of the burden of having to teach me?

_____

_____

_____

_____

How can I practice acknowledging what I understand to be the case before asking for clarification with confident humility?

_____

_____

_____

_____

What cultural experiences have I seen in various media depictions that help me understand experiences I haven't shared personally?

_____

_____

_____

_____

Navigating Cultural Terms of Reference

Terms of reference refer to the words and labels used to describe categories of people (e.g., African American, Christian, cisgender). Given that some terms are associated with past negative experiences or have implications that are not appreciated by the person to whom they refer, it is often unclear what terms are most appropriate to identify groups of people. In response, some organizations have made extensive efforts to create lists of acceptable or preferred terms of reference. Unfortunately, these efforts, while well-intentioned, often fail to meet their intended goal. That's because what is considered acceptable or preferred differs over time, and terms that were commonly used a decade or two ago might be considered offensive today. Preferences can also vary by location. How people prefer to be identified in the South may be different than how people from the same cultural group prefer to be identified in the Midwest.

In addition, what is considered acceptable or preferred often differs across people within groups. Within a cultural group, it is common to have some people who prefer to be called one thing, while others in that same group prefer to be called something else. I remember leaving a large predominately African American high school to attend a largely White American university. During my student orientation, I overheard one student say to another, "Don't call me African American, call me Black." Mere minutes later, I found myself in another room, overhearing a different student express, "Don't call me Black, call me African American." I wasn't sure what I should even call myself. Naturally, it is understandable that those outside of a particular cultural group might not be completely sure what cultural terms of reference are best to use in any given situation.

This is a common term-of-reference dilemma with respect to how we identify ourselves, as well as how we should identify others. Is it better to use a broader term of reference, like Asian American, or wait until you learn enough information to use a more specific term of reference, such as Korean American, Chinese American, or Vietnamese American? Is it better to use White, White American, European American, or Caucasian? What about Hispanic, Latina, Latino, or Latinx?

Before deciding which terms of reference you should use for whom, it is helpful to acknowledge the extent to which these terms of reference are important to certain groups of people. To some, terms of reference are merely words. To others, they convey value and respect, or lack thereof, as well as the cherished history of the people to whom they refer. If you find that certain groups place a high value on particular terms, this need not result in a paralyzing fear of disrespect. Rather, you can convey your understanding of this value by making intentional efforts to refer to and identify others with cultural consideration and respect. The following are a few guiding principles to help you make term-of-reference decisions:

Be intentional and cautious about your choice of words. Whatever terms of reference you use, do so with intentionality. Make intentional efforts to learn as much as reasonably possible about the terms available, and make the best and most considerate choice based on the information you have. In doing so, you convey that you value how people are impacted by your choice. That way, if someone is offended by your preferred term and asks you, "Why would you use that offensive term?" you can respond appropriately. Instead of saying, "I don't know, I just picked something I heard someone else say," you can reply, "It was my understanding that this was the most considerate and respectful term available. If that is not the case for you, my apologies for the inconvenience. Please feel free to let me know how you'd prefer to be referred to, and I will modify accordingly."

Use the most respectful term available. Even if the person you are interacting with uses a less respectful term when referring to themselves and those they identify with, your choice to use the most respectful term available shows your value and respect for them as a person. It also demonstrates your desire to avoid unintentional offense by assuming a degree of familiarity you may not have yet earned.

Accept that there are terms that members of a certain cultural group can use, but you can't. Sometimes helping professionals fall into the common trap of believing that "If it's okay for you to use the term, then it should be okay for me to use the term." To some extent, this mindset has merit in the sense that if a term of reference has been deemed acceptable and even preferred, then don't fix what isn't broken, and use the preapproved term. At the same time, certain terms of reference have negative connotations because of the experiences associated with them. And not only that, but those past negative experiences are inextricably linked to interactions with certain other cultural groups. This is often the motivation behind the statement "It's okay when I say it, but you can't say it." This is not about hypocrisy. The meaning, significance, and value behind the term changes depending on who is using it. This is a common factor to consider in both healthy and unhealthy reactions in response to the usage of certain cultural terms of reference.

When in doubt, quote. In your professional effort to use the most respectful term available, you may inadvertently use terms that don't sufficiently convey true empathy and understanding. For example, you may have become most comfortable with using your preferred cultural terms of reference, such as African American and Caucasian. However, if those terms are not readily familiar to the person to whom you are trying to relate, then using those terms might result in a relational barrier. For example, while you might be more comfortable reflecting, "So as you mentioned before, African American and Caucasian relationships have been difficult in your community," it may cause your client to respond in confusion, "I'm not sure what you're talking about because I never use words like that."

In situations like these, it may be more beneficial to quote, "So as you mentioned before, Black and White relationships in your community have been difficult." The goal here is not to convey an unearned sense of familiarity—or disrespect and lack of care—for the potential significance of certain terms of reference. Rather, the goal is to prioritize the language that the client is more comfortable using *and* hearing to maximize empathy and understanding. While this may seem to some like an unprofessional choice to use a less sophisticated-sounding term, the choice to use the language with which the client is most comfortable may very well be the more considerate and cultural-identity-affirming gift to the person you're trying to help.

Avoid overgeneralizations. Another often unappreciated use of cultural terms of reference is overgeneralizations. This is evident in phrases such as "You people always..."—which are commonly deemed offensive. Often, these phrases are based on some opinion or individual experience that has been overgeneralized to describe an entire cultural group. And while many in that cultural group might even be willing to risk acknowledging the occasional validity of the overgeneralization, it is not this occasional acknowledgment of truth that causes offense. Rather, it is the absolute assumption that all people of any cultural group are exactly the same. This belief has the tendency to make people feel stripped of their individual and cultural identity, as well as to make them feel the need to defend any potential negative connotations of the overgeneralization.

You can reduce this trend by acknowledging the limitations of any perceived generalization. For example, you can replace "You people always..." with "It is my understanding that *it is common* for people from this particular cultural group to _____. Has that been your experience?" or even "It is my understanding that people from this particular cultural group *tend to* _____. Has that been your experience?" This strategy allows you to share the overgeneralized information and convey it in a respectful way while also welcoming correction or personalization, rather than conveying absolute truth that generates defensiveness.

When it comes to cultural terms of reference, I encourage you to learn as much as you can about the many ways people from various cultural groups (beyond ethnicity) prefer to be identified. Acknowledging that whatever you learn can and will likely change after you learn it can help you maintain a realistic perspective on the learning process. The following worksheet will help you explore how you can use cultural terms of reference with more intentionality.

Cultural Competency Journey Reflection

What cultural terms of reference do I consider to be the most considerate and respectful?

_____

_____

_____

_____

What cultural terms of reference do I want to be able to use but fear that it might be misunderstood or experienced in ways I don't intend?

_____

_____

_____

_____

How can I intentionally convey that my desire is to show consideration for others' cultural identity instead of using my preferred cultural terms of reference?

_____

_____

_____

_____

Social Justice:
Finding Your Role

One of the components of cultural competency listed earlier is also one of the most practical and action-oriented aspects: **social justice**. In practice, increased awareness of social injustices around the world has increased the need for helping professionals to assist in wrestling with the implications of these past and present events on cross-cultural relationship interactions, as well as on overall daily functioning. Unfortunately, many helping professionals feel unprepared to adequately address social justice and injustice concerns expressed by their clients, which can transcend political stances and reflect increased polarization. In light of such, I would like to focus here on the role that increased social justice awareness and action can play in healthy cultural competence growth among helping professionals.

Know Your Role: Advocate

While many therapists have ethical mandates to advocate for their clients, there are many forms in which this can manifest. For some, advocacy takes the form of civil activism (e.g., picketing, lobbying, and legislation efforts), where they intend to use their professional role to inform community and government leaders to make the necessary changes that will hopefully benefit their individual clients and their families.

For many other professionals, this type of activist advocacy is not in their personal or professional comfort zone. Unfortunately, this often leads many professionals to feel inadequate, as though they are not doing their part to truly advocate for others. However, activism is not the only true form of client advocacy; there are other legitimate forms of advocacy available. Advocacy involves acting on behalf of your client to improve their situation, which you can accomplish without leaving your specific professional role (e.g., one-on-one counseling, coaching, mentoring). For example, when you work with a teacher to reduce their anxiety and improve their self-care, you are supporting the creation of a healthier learning environment for the students they are entrusted to teach. When you work with a law enforcement officer to increase their self-awareness regarding cultural biases, you are advocating for every community member that officer encounters.

Whether you feel compelled to have more of an explicit or implicit advocacy role, you can contribute to the greater need for healthier cross-cultural interactions for your individual clients, as well as for your community.

Know Your Role: Support

When people in need seek out support from helping professionals, they tend to lay out all their perceived struggles, both internal and external, and request that the professional provide a clear and absolute solution. This can be particularly significant when clients' stress and anxiety are integrally related to social injustices (e.g., community safety concerns, distrust of authorities). In response to these genuine requests for help, helping professionals often feel pressure to provide societal solutions out of a sincere desire to improve the lives of their clients. Unfortunately, societal solutions are hard to come by and often not in the professional's power to control.

Instead of writing yourself off as useless to clients struggling with social justice concerns, it is vital to embrace the value of supporting your client in the midst of societal uncertainty and a lack of societal or global solutions. You will find that your caring efforts to understand, empathize with, and validate your client's experience—including their past experiences, present fears, and future hopes—can have a significant impact on their ability to cope with their circumstances and to feel empowered by the potential role they can play in larger efforts to make societal changes.

Know Your Role: Empathize

Although empathy is an important relationship-building skill, it is particularly beneficial as it relates to navigating the often-polarizing world of social justice. In your efforts to build, maintain, and repair cross-cultural relationships, the goal is to **learn to empathize with both sides of any controversy**. To be clear, the goal is not to agree with both sides or to affirm the truth or accuracy of both sides. Rather, with an emphasis on the people behind the polarizing words, actions, and policies, the goal is to be as open as possible to learning about the feelings and motivations behind those words, actions, and policies. Applying this kind of empathy to emotionally charged social justice situations can increase the likelihood that you will see past the vilification of opposing views and identify recommendations for change that are mutually beneficial.

THE VICTIM & THE ACCUSED

Consider… An incident that occurred in a high school on the East Coast, which made national news. Cell phone camera footage captured a White male school police officer grabbing a desk, while an African American female student was in it, and flinging it across a room to remove her from the chair. This footage generated lots of controversy regarding why such force was used. Because the video clip was brief, there was no evidence showing justification for the officer's actions, nor was there any evidence confirming a preceding behavior on the student's part that warranted such action. Nonetheless, polarizing responses arose around the country either defending the officer (making assumptions about the student's behavior and guilt) or defending the student (making assumptions about the officer's behavior and guilt).

Now imagine the following hypothetical scenario: A few days after the incident, a therapist meets a new client and discovers that it's the student from the video. Realizing the significance of the incident in that client's life and acknowledging that this incident is not an experience that the therapist shares, the therapist makes intentional efforts to put aside personal conclusions and seeks to begin building a professional helping relationship with this student. Later in the day, the therapist meets another new client: the school police officer. After exploring potential ethical barriers, the therapist decides to move forward with seeing this new client as well, making similar efforts to put aside personal conclusions to build a professional helping relationship with this client too.

The therapist helps both clients achieve different goals. The student is able to gain a better understanding of her own identity as an individual, a family member, a student, and a community member. And the therapist helps the police officer by listening to him recount the incident and what preceded it. In doing so, the therapist learns that the officer, who operated in his role with a genuine desire to protect and serve, found himself faced with a difficult school safety issue that was getting out of hand and the responsibility to ensure that it stayed managed. The officer expresses regret for his choice and also for the potential impact it had on the student. The therapist validates his experience and the difficult position his job placed him in. She helps him identify personal and professional blinders that limited his ability to respond to this challenging situation while also helping him develop other options for responding to challenges in the future.

As helping professionals, we face a similar challenge on a regular basis: to empathize with both sides of any controversy. Maybe you'll be referred a client with a history of incarceration, domestic violence, or other experiences people are often more inclined to judge than support. Regardless of where your client stands—whether they are considered to be the abuser, the abused, or the falsely accused—your challenge is still to make every effort to empathize with the person behind the behavior. It's not about approving the rightness or wrongness of the behavior. It is about learning about the person behind the behaviors, their history, and the motivations that contributed to their actions. It is here where change can occur. People cannot change the past, but they can influence the present and the future by providing less judgment and more support to others.

Oftentimes, past cultural experiences and misunderstandings cause people to exhibit behaviors in the present moment that are motivated by a desire to protect themselves against perceived threats. However, if that perceived threat is actually a misunderstanding, then that person's well-intentioned action to protect themselves can come across as an unwarranted act of aggression. Cultivating increased cultural awareness and consideration not only reduces the likelihood of these occurrences in the first place, but it can also help identify offensive actions influenced by cultural ignorance rather than malicious or racist intent.

TO RUN OR NOT TO RUN

Consider... a large green community park, lined with intersecting cement pathways, where a group of ethnic minority young adults is casually hanging out, laughing, and joking about recent events in their lives. Unexpectedly, they hear the loud and telltale *whoop whoop* of a police car as it drives up and stops at the park's edge. When an officer announces over the car's bullhorn for the group to stay where they are, the young men do the exact opposite, instantly scattering in different directions and running as fast as they can to wherever they think they can disappear.

After one of those young men runs a safe distance away— ensuring that he hasn't been followed—he slows his pace and walks home as calmly as possible. A little while later, this same young man finds himself recounting the story of this experience to a classmate who happens to be of a different ethnicity. This classmate responds by asking, "If you didn't do anything wrong, why did you run? Running makes you look guilty."

To this, the young man replies, "I know running doesn't look good, but based on what I have witnessed or heard about from witnesses of other incidents, the police officers' actions suggested that, to them, we looked guilty already. And if that is true, then I believe that, when they approached me in the park, the odds were high that I would have gotten slammed to the ground, asphalt pressed into my cheek, with a knee in my back, and potentially dragged into the back of a police car. The best-case scenario is that after searching my record, they would have realized that I had no record and would have let me go. But they would have justified their actions by saying that they put me through that because I fit the description of someone they were looking for.

"The worst-case scenario is that I would have accidentally made a sudden movement that heightened their existing fear for their lives, and they would have ended my life (with low odds of any legal repercussions). Now I could stay there and let all of those highly likely undesirable scenarios take place and hope for the best, or I could run and change my odds to 50/50. If I get caught, then the original scenarios still occur. If I get away, then I have avoided the worst-case scenario altogether—after all, they aren't actually looking for me specifically since I did nothing wrong."

Some helping professionals hear this story and unfortunately get stuck on seemingly right and wrong behaviors, while others make the most of the opportunity to gain understanding and empathy for behaviors that are not motivated by disrespect for authority but by perceived survival and protective measures.

ISOLATED EVENTS

Consider... a peaceful gathering that is taking place outside of a courthouse. After several hours, a clerk exits the courthouse and hands a file to a law enforcement public relations spokesperson, who relays that the verdict has come in: The court has decided not to indict the police officers who took the life of an innocent person.

Hearing the collective gasp from the crowd, the news media that are outside the courthouse turn their cameras to the crowd, looking to see how they react. Will they catch live footage of a riot breaking out, resulting in the destruction of property and maybe even causing injury people along the way? To the shock and disappointment of the news media, the dejected and angry crowd turns and disperses, expressing their frustrations to one another as they return home. Before leaving, one of the news personalities addresses one of the protestors: "Did you know the victim personally? Was he family or a close friend?" When the protestor responds to the contrary, the news reporter asks, "So then why do you care so much, especially since it was just an isolated event?" In response, the protestor calmly expresses, "Because I don't want to be the next isolated event."

For many, incidents such as these understandably seem like isolated events. After all, it is not a common occurrence in their daily lives, and the news media rarely covers these events, so some people are genuinely confused why certain communities are impacted so significantly by these events. First, it is important to acknowledge there are many cultural experiences that are not exhaustively covered by the news media, so just because the media isn't covering it, doesn't mean it isn't happening more often than you think. Second, although incidents deemed worthy of national headlines may not occur on a daily basis, the precipitating events and contributing circumstances to these events are often experienced as a normal and constant aspect of life for many communities in this country. This can lead to the slow buildup of tension and racial divides. Some of these contributing experiences include:

- **Poverty:** When people lack the financial resources to meet their own needs and their family's needs, they often experience feelings of desperation that compel them to do things they never thought they would do if they didn't believe it was necessary for their survival.

- **Community homelessness and hopelessness:** People who are homeless often arrive at that state through various paths. Not only can people become homeless despite much legitimate effort to the contrary, but once in that state, it can be much more difficult to overcome than people with a home seem to understand. Moreover, when efforts to overcome homelessness move so slowly that they seem to be stagnant or regressing, homelessness can grow into hopelessness, which has the potential to negatively influence decision making.

- **Unemployment and underemployment:** Even if someone has a place to call home, when they lack sufficient financial resources to care for themselves and their family, this can have a significant impact on their sense of self-esteem and their perceived prospects for the future. It is particularly difficult for those who work multiple jobs totaling more than 50 hours per week but who receive less than a livable wage in return. In addition, individuals in this situation frequently experience judgment and lack of compassion because people assume that their lack of employment is due to laziness, resulting in their refusal to empathize or provide support in any way.

- **Being uninsured or underinsured:** For many individuals, their first response to undesirable physical discomfort or pain is to make a call to a nurse's line or take a trip to a primary care physician. This is made possible by the reassurance that comes from having sufficient medical insurance coverage. However, those who lack sufficient insurance make this decision based on the severity of their symptoms, and depending on what they deem worth the risk, they may put off medical care, resulting in long-term damage. It's not that these individuals don't care about their physical well-being. Rather, the reality is that not everyone has the luxury to "just go get a check-up" because copays, deductibles, and premiums cost more than many families have.

- **Undereducation:** Just as limitations in housing and insurance can impact quality of life, so can lack of education. There was once a time when all you needed was a high school diploma in order to find reasonable employment that would provide a livable wage and the ability to maintain a healthy lifestyle. Now there are individuals who have completed high school, college, and graduate school yet find it difficult to obtain sufficient employment to meet the reasonable needs of their household.

- **Limited examples to emulate:** *Representation* is a word often used in conversations about diversity, equity, and inclusion in relation to business policies and procedures. At the community level, it can be very empowering, inspiring, and impactful to have the opportunity to see people who look like you who have accomplished great things in their lives. **It increases your belief in your ability to accomplish similar things**. After all, when people in certain professional roles only look a certain way—and that way is different than how children in certain communities see themselves—it is understandable why many children conclude that pursuing those types of careers is an effort in futility. They may believe that "Those careers aren't for people like me" or "People who look like me don't do that." Not only is it likely that this perception is untrue, but all it takes is one person to be the first for others to see that it's possible.

- **Overdiagnosis:** As a mental health professional, I have had the opportunity to support many parents as they wrestle with the dilemma of whether or not to "allow" their child to be diagnosed with a mental health disorder, particularly attention or disruptive behavior–related disorders. This dilemma is often motivated by a genuine desire to do what is in their child's best interest. For example, if their child's behaviors would improve if mental health services were provided, then a diagnosis serves as symptom verification that justifies the need for those services. However, if their child's behavioral difficulties are more indicative of a teacher's misunderstanding of culturally appropriate behaviors (which are outside of the teacher's personal, family, or community norms), then the parent may be more hesitant. This type of hesitancy is understandable given that ethnic minority students are disproportionately diagnosed with mental health disorders, and teachers tend to have lower expectations of these students and, in turn, are less invested in them. In the end, it is often not the mental health disorder itself that parents are cautious about but the possibility that the diagnosis will result in a decreased investment in their child's success and ultimately their future.

- **Disproportionate suspensions and expulsions:** Just as there are a disproportionate number of ethnic minority students diagnosed with mental disorders, there is inequality when it comes to which students get suspended and expelled from school. A Brown Center Report showed that students of color are disproportionately dealt the harshest exclusionary penalties, such as expulsions and out-of-school suspensions (Loveless, 2017). And a federal report by the U.S. Government Accountability Office suggests that implicit bias causes Black male students to be disciplined at school more than their White counterparts (2018). It is trends like these that contribute to the reality that some students don't feel like educational professionals—to whom they are entrusted—are actually invested in their educational future. This lack of trust and the consequences that result from this leads to a lack of educational success among ethnic minority students.

- **Racial profiling by law enforcement:** It is important to note here that I respect and appreciate the difficult challenge law enforcement officers have in discerning and preventing threats on a daily basis. Despite those efforts, there is room for growth in light of research showing that a disproportionate number of ethnic minority drivers are pulled over compared to White Americans. This is such a common experience that communities are integrally familiar with terms such as DWB (i.e., Driving While Black), while other communities are more familiar with DWH (i.e., Driving While Hispanic). These terms serve as shorthand for the research-supported belief that people from ethnic minorities are singled out, not because of any legitimate wrongdoing but because officers see them as more suspicious than someone else, based on their ethnicity. Even without verifiable proof of the individual motivation and circumstances that lead to each experience, the impact nonetheless influences people's trust in law enforcement. When certain groups of people are given unwarranted attention, this naturally increases the likelihood that their law enforcement encounter may end poorly.

- **Disproportionate numbers of individuals arrested, prosecuted, and given harsher punishments for the same crimes:** Speaking of ending poorly, similar to research showing that ethnic minority individuals are pulled over by police officers at a higher frequency, there is also research reflecting how...

...If pulled over, ethnic minority individuals have an increased likelihood of being **arrested** than White individuals.

...If arrested, ethnic minority individuals have an increased likelihood of being **charged** with a crime than White individuals.

...If charged, ethnic minority individuals have an increased likelihood of being **convicted** of a crime than White individuals.

...If convicted of a crime, ethnic minority individuals have an increased likelihood of being **punished more harshly** than White individuals.

To be clear, this is not an indictment on any specific officer or judge. Rather, this is reflective of a larger systemic problem that is more difficult to identify, and thus more difficult to change, yet is nonetheless supported by the resulting statistics. I am not suggesting that certain groups of people are always right or always wrong; there are individuals from every cultural group who sometimes behave in ways that justify the need for law enforcement to maintain order in our society. That is to say that arrests, charges, convictions, and punishments are sometimes necessary. However, accountability must be in place to ensure that these measures are taken regardless of an individual's cultural background, rather than being influenced by misperceptions and unconscious negative cultural biases.

Discerning Your Social Justice Role

In light of these realities, it is essential to remember that the role of helping professionals is not to solve every societal problem. Rather, it's to empathize with and support individuals as they wrestle with discerning the things they can change while also recognizing the things they cannot change. Before helping your client find the change they can make in their lives, you must first accept that individuals from various communities may experience circumstances that produce tensions and fears and that attempted solutions to those tensions and fears may or may not rest in your professional comfort zone.

Some helping professionals even go so far as to genuinely reassure others' anxieties with expressions of "Don't worry, you're overreacting. It'll all work out" or "Just trust the system." While these statements are well-meaning, they unfortunately miss the fact that differing experiences (both direct and indirect) often justify trust or lack thereof in the system. You don't need to prove or disprove another's fears to help them realize what is within their power to change and to then encourage them to make those changes, both internally and externally.

In addition to the challenge of finding their own role in social justice matters, many helping professionals also struggle when it comes to helping clients wrestle with *their* role in social justice issues. It can be easy to give into the temptation to lean a client toward your own preferences and comfort level and to find more support for the legitimacy of certain ideas over others. You can avoid this temptation by building off the empathy skills discussed earlier and making intentional efforts to see both sides of social justice controversies, as well as their possible responses. We must acknowledge that our preferences and biases influence what is obvious to us. When we refuse to be limited by such, we can intentionally look for the pros and cons of our preferred ideas, as well as the ideas with which we are less comfortable. This process can help us see that opposing viewpoints don't have to be polarized into a winning and losing side or a right and wrong side. This can be the beginning of choosing the best available option at the time, while still respecting the merit or genuine motivation behind other ideas and recommendations.

CONSTRUCTIVE DISRUPTION

Consider... the following true story regarding a Black Lives Matter protest. A few years ago, prior to the beginning of the Minnesota State Fair, one of the largest state fairs in the country, a local Black Lives Matter group provided advanced notice to the police, as well as the media, that they were planning a protest to coincide with the state fair. Their detailed plans included a peaceful march to the entry gate of the state fair. There they would gather, one or more of the group's leaders would say a few words to the crowd, and then they would disperse.

On the day of the protest, things went according to plan. There was a peaceful march during which streets were temporarily blocked, and cars full of families eagerly waiting their turn to participate in the fair were inconvenienced. Even though the protesters gathered at the entrance to the fair, they still made room for people to enter and exit the fair. Business was still able to continue, but people were inconvenienced. The flow was disrupted.

Media personnel asked fair attendees about their impressions of the protest. Many were genuinely confused, wondering why anyone would want to disrupt an event whose sole purpose was to support the gathering of families and communities in a fun way. The same media personnel found their way to one of the leaders of the protest and inquired as to the motivation for the protest.

The leader indicated that this protest was intended to bring attention to the inequalities in the application process for which vendors were accepted into the state fair. Put more simply, the percentage of ethnic minority–owned businesses that were approved and accepted as vendors was significantly lower than the percentage of ethnic minority–owned businesses that applied. Prior to the protest, multiple attempts to address this discrepancy with state fair organizers were dismissed or minimized, with responses conveying that the fair vendor application process, which had been used for years, was fair and colorblind, implying that protestors should simply trust the process. Since this direct approach didn't motivate leaders toward change, they planned a protest for the explicit purpose of a gaining broader platform.

After the protest, the media gained the attention of the leaders of the state fair. In addition to asking the usual questions about the popularity of the fair (e.g., the featured animals, fried foods, and family fun activities), they also asked about the response to the protestors, the application process, and whether intentional efforts were being made to support a variety of business. The protest brought greater attention to an issue that previously held a limited audience (Pioneer Press, 2015).

Imagine you have a client who is wrestling with finding their role in response to a recent social justice issue (e.g., a police shooting in their community that received mass media attention). This person expresses wanting to be a part of a protest happening the following night. Whether or not you're inclined toward more direct or indirect advocacy, it is important to take the time to understand and empathize with your client's motivation and intent behind this decision.

In this particular scenario, there is often a misunderstanding between a riot and a protest. Put simply: **A protest is a healthy expression of feeling, while a riot is an unhealthy expression of feeling**. The feeling is legitimate either way; however, it's how that feeling is expressed behaviorally that determines its impact. Consider the earlier state fair protest, where their goal was to inconvenience others in order to bring attention to a significant issue that was otherwise being overlooked or minimized. If your client expresses a desire to participate in an upcoming protest—and your mind goes straight to looting and destroying property—then your efforts to steer them toward healthier behaviors might be misguided. Instead, take the time to explore their frustrations and past experiences, along with their desires for better future experiences. Then help them find the best role they can play in order to change their situation. You don't need to have shared their experiences or their desperation for change to help them find the healthiest way to express their feelings and bring about positive social change.

But Don't *All* Lives Matter?

One final social justice recommendation is to remember that law enforcement officers are imperfect people too. In our often polarizing society, there is a compulsion to choose between opposing sides. As I have consistently shown, while you can feel free to choose your values and priorities, you don't have to support the polarization of those views over someone else's values and priorities.

The Black Lives Matter movement is often a source of confusion as a result of polarizing views. For some, when people hear someone assert, "Black lives matter!" they often feel compelled to respond, "All lives matter!" This response reflects a misunderstanding of the Black Lives Matter message. The message is not intended to convey that Black lives matter *more* than other lives. Rather, it is to point out that Black lives have experienced a disproportionate amount of discrimination, injustice, mistreatment, aggression, and minimization, so much so that it seems and feels as though their lives do *not* matter to the larger society. Therefore, saying "all lives matter" fails to acknowledge the experience of many Black people for whom this message has not been true. All lives do matter equally, but not all lives have been treated as though they matter.

This dilemma also applies to the genuine assertion that blue lives matter, referring to law enforcement personnel. When people assert that "Blue lives matter!" in response to the statement "Black lives matter!" this has the potential to be misunderstood as if one is expressing that law enforcement personnel (i.e., blue lives) matter *more* than Black lives. In reality, all lives indeed matter, and this need not be expressed as a correction or higher priority. When the statement "Blue lives matter" is not expressed as a counterargument to Black lives matter, there is genuine merit to the message that blue lives matter.

Consider the incident in 2016 where police officers were ambushed and fired upon—five officers were killed and nine were injured—by a man who admitted his motivation was his anger at White police officers following the fatal police shootings of Alton Sterling and Philando Castile (which had occurred two days prior). There have been many others who have expressed aggressive sentiments toward law enforcement officers following events such as these. In fact, there have been many growing assertions that physical harm should come to law enforcement officers in order to teach them a lesson. In turn, many individuals—in defense of their lives—have felt genuinely compelled to assert that "Blue lives matter!" It is worth noting that the officers in the ambush incident were not involved in the police shootings that motivated the reported "retaliatory" response.

Similar to the protest versus riot distinction, there are healthy and unhealthy ways to express feelings. People who feel compelled to commit physical and even life-threatening harm against law enforcement personnel may be motivated by protective feelings and desperate desires for legitimate change, but they are ultimately expressing these feelings in an unhealthy manner. There are many law enforcement officers who disapprove of the misuse of authority by their peers and who are making intentional efforts not to perpetuate those behaviors and to discourage those behaviors instead.

Unfortunately, these accountability efforts have yet to bring about long-lasting systematic change. While the answer to this problem may not be clear, as helping professionals, I urge you to be cautious about providing quick-fix solutions to broader dilemmas such as these. For example, some have offered the simple recommendation that we increase training for law enforcement personnel. However, many find recommendations like these to be insufficient. Some go so far as to justify physical retaliation by arguing that police officers "need to know what it feels like to be afraid"—their reasoning being that if law enforcement officers knew, understood, and empathized with the fear generated by experiences of law enforcement, then they would naturally feel compelled to change their ways. Unfortunately, this theory of change fails to take into account that many law enforcement officers are already afraid.

YOU'RE MAKING US LOOK BAD

Consider... a law enforcement officer in a large city, who is genuinely grateful for the opportunity to have a career in law enforcement that fulfils what has felt like a lifelong calling. On a daily basis, this officer leaves home hopeful for the opportunity to prevent someone from being taken advantage of or harmed. Also on a daily basis, this same officer leaves home not knowing whether he will return home safely or not at all due to the malicious or negligent actions of someone else.

One morning, as this officer prepares to leave for work, the morning news reports an incident involving a police shooting of an unarmed ethnic minority community member. As the story goes on, this officer has multiple thoughts. First, he feels sorrow for the loss of life involved. Second, he questions whether or not the officer involved was acting maliciously, negligently, or professionally. Finally, he acknowledges the personal implications of this incident, leading him to think, *You're making us look bad. How will this incident impact how I am seen by those in the community? Will someone try to hurt me today because of what this officer did?*

As helping professionals, we need to intentionally consider experiences like these without giving in to stereotypes. Remember: Law enforcement officers are imperfect people too. Many of them are well-meaning individuals who pursued a career for genuine motivations to protect and serve those in their community. That being said, there are law enforcement professionals—just as there are those in other high-stakes careers—who have deviated from that motivation and who are doing more harm than good. There is no all-or-nothing stereotype that we can place on law enforcement officers as a whole. Therefore, we should learn to balance empathizing with individuals and treating them the way they deserve be treated, while also making efforts toward systematic change. **The goal is to create understanding that leads to change, rather than condemnation that leads to retaliation and polarization.**

There is likely no one-size-fits-all solution to this ongoing dilemma. Fortunately, your measure of success as a helping professional is not in finding a solution. You have the challenge of first taking the time and making the effort to understand and empathize with both sides of every argument—not to justify both sides but to understand why varying perspectives matter to those who hold them. Then, one client at a time, help those whom you have the opportunity to help. No matter the cultural differences between you and your client, you can come alongside them and help them improve their lives and potentially the lives of their families and greater communities as well.

You can reflect on your own advocacy efforts, including your ability to empathize with opposing social justice perspectives, using the worksheet on the next page.

Cultural Competency Journey Reflection

Am I inclined toward activism-oriented advocacy or more one-on-one support-oriented advocacy? Why?

_____

_____

_____

_____

What social justice concerns am I aware of today? What are the various perspectives people have about these issues, and how can I practice empathizing with the people behind these various perspectives?

_____

_____

_____

_____

What opportunities do I have to see the validity in others' feelings and motivations without approving or invalidating others' actions?

_____

_____

_____

_____

Common Ethnic Group Characteristics

Thus far, you have been provided a practical foundation for a healthy understanding of cultural diversity and cultural competence, as well as practical strategies for addressing cultural offenses and repairing relationships. With these new or enhanced insights, you are equipped to significantly improve the quality and longevity of your cross-cultural professional and personal relationships.

In this final section, I will address some common cultural group experiences, myths, and misunderstandings. This is not intended to be a stereotyped list that provides you with complete summaries of all the likes and dislikes of each cultural group. It is also not even a complete list of all possible cultural groups. As I mentioned earlier, what constitutes a cultural group grows with our understanding of various life experiences. This section is intended to merely get you started on what will hopefully be a lifelong journey of never-ending cultural learning. What matters most is not the multitude of categories into which we can fit people. Rather, it's about making intentional efforts to learn more about others in our community and around the world.

Given that no ethnic cultural group has characteristics that apply to absolutely everyone in that group, learning and memorizing ethnic group characteristics will always be a limited endeavor. There are countless ethnic groups and subsets of ethnic groups to learn about. It is also an endeavor that should be made cautiously, as focusing too much on common ethnic group characteristics can tempt us to believe ethnic group stereotypes in a way that hinders our ability to truly see, understand, and empathize with the individual, couple, or family we are trying to serve.

Although deliberate caution is warranted, fear is not. Just because there are exceptions doesn't mean there is no merit to there being common (though not absolute) ethnic group experiences and characteristics. Make the most of opportunities to learn about patterns of cultural values, norms, customs, traditions, and language (both verbal and nonverbal). Practice tactfully using this information to help facilitate healthy cross-cultural rapport. And expect there to be exceptions to the norms you have learned.

Diverse Families

Many people consider their family to be their primary cultural group, where norms, values, and preferred ways of living are formed and cultivated. Some helping professionals work for organizations that have the word *family* in their name. However, a prudent question arises as to whether that organization provides services to all families or just a select few. For example, when some say the word *family*, they instinctively picture a traditional two-parent, heterosexual, monocultural nuclear family household. And while that fits or comes close to the family experience of many in this country, it does not reflect many other family compositions. With variations in family makeup also come variations in family values, norms, strengths, growth areas, fears, and hopes. Therefore, professionals who are seeking to effectively serve "families" would benefit from broadening their perspective on whom clients consider to be family. Let's take a look at a few variations on family composition.

Multiethnic families may include families where partners come from different ethnic cultural backgrounds. Within multiethnic families, parents often have the challenge of determining which customs and values the children will identify with more. As a helping professional, you may be tasked with helping the family explore the significance of their values and helping them find their own way of respecting one another's values. In addition, you may need to help the parents explore the weight they place on their children embracing their cultural identity. Sometimes this is accomplished in healthy ways. Other times, barriers get in the way, such as the disapproval of family members whose preferences have historically held more weight in their broader family system. In circumstances such as these, you may be asked to help the individual set and achieve healthy goals, find contentment within their chosen family expectations, gain family support for their preferred future goals, or achieve their goals without the degree of family support they desire. What is most important is empowering them to make the decision regarding which options they would like your help pursuing.

LGBTQ+ couples have received increased visibility over the years. If your professional services will be offered to families, you must also consider the needs of same-sex couples. Some professionals argue that their services don't apply to same-sex couples because these couples have unique needs that require specialized services. While certain cultural experiences may require more specific services, this in no way rules out services that can benefit every family (e.g., improved communication skills). Helping professionals who are willing to learn from their clients can discover how to apply their services to same-sex couples and their families.

Immigrant families face unique challenges compared to non-immigrant families, including spousal, parenting, and other common family dynamic challenges; language challenges (where the language spoken in the home may be different from that required to obtain sufficient resources outside of the home); and citizenship challenges (which have the potential to impact access to resources and contribute to fear of deportation). Helping professionals have the challenge of separating their political beliefs from their efforts to empathize with the present struggles of immigrant families.

The number of **cohabitating couples** (unmarried couples living together) has increased significantly, according to the U.S. Census Bureau (Gurrentz, 2018). Whether this is due to changes in marital values, the reduction of stigma associated with living together outside of marriage, or financial necessity, cohabiting couples are becoming increasingly common. These couples face similar challenges to those of married couples, including similar co-parenting challenges. A major difference, however, is that there are often relationship implications when couples do not have a shared commitment to the relationship as is reflected in marriage. At the same time, it would be a mistake to assume that *all* cohabitating couples lack sufficient commitment simply because they have not chosen to marry. It is important to empathize with the unique needs of the particular cohabiting couple.

Single-parent families have continued to become more common, as reported by the U.S. Census Bureau (Vanorman & Jacobsen, 2020). Parents can become single parents for a variety of reasons, whether it's the death of a partner or spouse, the loss of a spouse's daily presence due to incarceration, a mother's choice to get pregnant via artificial insemination outside of a committed relationship, or the ending of a committed relationship that results in one parent being primarily responsible for raising the child. Regardless of the origin of the single-parent family, quality parenting and healthy parent-child relationships are still possible and occur on a regular basis. As helping professionals, we must acknowledge the unique challenges of having only one parent in the home while also maximizing that single parent's strengths. It is important to assist in whatever way possible to help that parent and child(ren) cultivate a healthy family that can be a solid foundation from which to build the rest of their lives.

Multigenerational households are households where more than two generations reside (e.g., children, parents, and grandparents). There are various reasons why multigenerational households exist. Sometimes it is due to health concerns, which is often the case when grandparents need more care than they would receive living on their own, but an assisted living facility is either undesired, financially unavailable, or contrary to cultural family values. Sometimes childcare is the primary motivation. In these situations, the parents need assistance in taking care of the child, and daycare is either financially or otherwise unavailable. The parents may also have a strong appreciation for the bonding opportunities that this would offer the grandparents. Other times, an adult child may have difficulty finding sufficient employment to afford moving into their own home, leading them to live with their parents.

When working with multigenerational households, you may be called upon to help families find a healthy balance when it comes to shared authority between the parents and grandparents. You may also work with families where grandparents wrestle with how they are being treated, as their now-adult children may treat them similarly to how they parent their own children. Regardless of the origin of the family's household makeup, it is important to take the time to learn how the family's multigenerational household status came to be, to examine the value the family places on having multiple generations in the home, and to understand its impact on the family system.

Households in which **grandparents are raising grandchildren** are similar to multigenerational households in that the origins of these households differ widely. Sometimes grandparents raise grandchildren because the child's parents are deceased or incarcerated. There are also times when child abuse leads to loss of parental custody, compelling a grandparent to become the guardian. In situations like these, grandparents are sometimes motivated by the fear that foster care symbolizes the loss of any future relationship with their grandchildren. Other times, they believe that taking care of the grandchildren—instead of having them put into foster care—will increase the likelihood that the children's parents will successfully regain custody once they have turned their lives around.

Although grandparents' motivations and origins may differ, they face similar challenges in raising their grandchildren. They must establish healthy authority relationships in the home and also help their grandchildren process the absence of their parents. As a helping professional, it is important that your policies and practices are inclusive of grandparents who are serving in a guardian capacity. Sometimes it can involve reconsidering organizational rules that only allow biological parents to authorize treatment of a minor child, as well as modifying forms to include "or guardian" next to the signature line. Changes such as these can make a nonbiological parent feel seen and valued.

Families with adopted or foster children broaden the conversation even further when it comes to the unique benefits and challenges that nonbiological parents and their children face. It is commonly believed that children fare best when raised by their biological parents, but does this cancel out the potential positive impact of being raised by foster or adoptive parents? Most orphaned children would rather have the chance to live with a loving foster or adoptive family than remain in an orphanage for the remainder of their childhood.

As helping professionals, we need to make intentional efforts to convey the value and significance of family in its various forms, rather than treating foster and adoptive families as though they are not "real" families. It is also good to remember that, as it relates to terms of reference, some foster and adoptive families refer to one another differently. Some choose not to use descriptors such as "my foster mother" or "my adoptive father" in favor of simply calling them their mother and father. Often this is to convey the value and significance that the child places on the relationship. Other times, it's because the child's biological parents are no longer (or never were) a part of their lives. Other families choose to keep the "adoptive" and "foster" descriptors because the child's biological parents remain in their lives, and there is a desire to maintain the significance of that relationship as well.

Blended families are a unique blend of biological parents and nonbiological parents (e.g., stepparents, stepchildren, stepsiblings), with one or both partners bringing children from a previous relationship into their new family partnership. Although most families struggle with children who challenge authority—for example, a child may test boundaries and pit parents between each other to get their way—blended families have the added challenge of a child expressing to their nonbiological parent in frustration, "You can't tell me what to do! You're not my real parent!"

Therefore, parents in blended families must establish a unified front that clearly conveys what authority role each parent will take. Whether the couple prefers to share discipline responsibilities equally—or whether the child's biological parents prefer to be responsible for certain roles—it is key that the parents are in agreement. They must support each other in their established preferences and reduce misunderstandings from mixed messages by clearly conveying their position to their children. As helping professionals, we need to be able to support the family's preferred co-parenting style, even if it differs from what we would do if we were in their shoes. This is especially true if the family's preferences are influenced by cultural values that we do not share.

Interfaith couples, in which each partner holds different faith beliefs, are fairly common, with research finding that one in five U.S. adults were raised in an interfaith home (Pew Research Center, 2016). When it comes to interfaith couples, both partners may hold differing faith beliefs, or one partner may hold a certain faith belief while the other has no faith beliefs at all. These couples experience some unique family dynamic challenges, as questions often arise whether aspects of both faith beliefs will be shared together as a family, whether the family will choose one belief and let go of the other, or whether it will reflect some combination of their choosing. Sometimes this decision is influenced less by the couple's willingness to compromise with each other and more by differing concerns and hopes for how their children will be raised. Other times, the decision is based on the reality that faith beliefs mean significantly more to one partner than the other.

Even if a couple doesn't come to a concrete decision on the matter, that often lasts only until a significant faith-based holiday arises, which naturally prompts them to discuss and decide whether (and how) to celebrate that and other holidays. Research shows that almost half of U.S. adults consider shared faith beliefs to be very important for a successful marriage (Pew Research Center, 2016), so interfaith couples also often wrestle with discerning whether the relationship can last without shared faith beliefs (e.g., "Although I love you deeply, my faith and my faith community are a huge part of my life, and if we can't share that part of our lives together, I'm not sure if we can have a future together"). As a helping professional, your responsibility is not to tell the couple the right answer but to learn about their values, concerns, and hopes and to support the couple by helping them identify a plan for their future that is tailored to their needs.

Finally, **families without children** often face challenges associated with having to justify that a couple *can* be a family without having children. This is evident in the common question that childless couples face: "So when are you going to start a family?" People asking this question often don't realize that there are multiple reasons why a couple might not have children. For example, they may have tried to conceive but were hindered by fertility difficulties, or one of the partners may have experienced abuse prior to entering the relationship, which now poses a barrier to having children. The couple may have also mutually decided to accomplish certain personal or career goals prior to having children, or they may have decided that having children is not one of their essential life priorities. It is also possible that they may have had a child who has since passed away.

As a helping professional, you have the challenge of learning and empathizing with each of these motivations and supporting the couple in accomplishing their mutual goals. In addition, you may be tasked with helping the couple establish a healthy view of their relationship so when they're asked, "When are you going to start a family?" they can confidently respond, "The two of us together *are* a family. When or if we decide to have children won't change that."

Use the following worksheet to examine your current understanding of what it means to be a family, as well as to reflect on how you can broaden your perspective of what constitutes a healthy family.

Cultural Competency Journey Reflection

When I hear the word *family*, what picture of family comes to mind? What significance does family hold for me?

_____

_____

_____

_____

What types of families are hardest for me to understand, value, and empathize with?

_____

_____

_____

_____

What opportunities do I have to learn more about how others experience family so I can increase my understanding and empathy for healthy family experiences that differ from my idea of a healthy family?

_____

_____

_____

_____

Multiethnic Families

A Pew Research Center study revealed that 17 percent of new marriages in the U.S. include partners who marry a person of a different ethnicity, which represents a more than fivefold increase from 1967 (Livingston & Brown, 2017). If you include all married people in the U.S. (not just newlyweds), 10 percent of wedded couples are married to a person of a different ethnicity. Therefore, whether or not multiethnic families make up a large percentage of your clientele, as a helping professional, you would be well-served to learn about the similarities and differences of multiethnic families in preparation for the increasing likelihood that you will be called upon to meet their needs.

Terms of Reference

Regarding terms of reference for multiethnic families, while not an absolute rule, *interracial* and *multiethnic* are two terms with the least likelihood of cultural offense. *Mixed* and *biracial* are common terms as well, but varying responses suggest they be used selectively. For example, *mixed* is a term of reference that some consider to be a very descriptive term of reference (e.g., "I am a mix of my mother and father"), while others have experienced the term being used in derogatory ways.

Similarly, *biracial* is a term of reference that some believe to have diminished benefit because it is less descriptive than often intended. This is the case because the term is binary in nature and assumes there is a 50-50 split between two distinct ethnic backgrounds. However, one needs to look no further than the rise in DNA testing to see how no one is exactly 100 percent or a perfect 50-50 split of any particular ethnic group. Rather, there are unique combinations of ethnic backgrounds in us all. Therefore, while many still like and identify with the term, and have no problem with others using it, there are many who prefer to use terms without these limitations, such as *multiethnic* and *interracial*.

As with all terms of reference, it is essential that we remember these are merely starting points for personal understanding and relationship interaction. Instead of trying to learn and memorize right and wrong terms for what all people in a certain group prefer to be called, it is best to learn the motivations behind their preferences and aversions and to learn comfortable ways to invite others to tell you how they prefer to be referenced.

The Stigma Continues

When increasing your effectiveness in meeting the needs of multiethnic couples, one thing to realize is that multiethnic couples don't yet receive universal acceptance in this country. A Gallup Poll revealed that 87 percent of Americans report that they approve of marriages between White and Nonwhite persons (Newport, 2013). For many multiethnic couples, this statistic is reassuring, especially considering that it reflects nearly a twofold increase since 1994. However, a few concerns remain even with statistics such as these. For example, if 87 percent of Americans approve of interracial marriage, that leaves 13 percent who don't. Not only that, but what statistics and research fail to capture is the difference between people's ideological views and their practical daily actions. For example, there are some people who genuinely express their acceptance of interracial marriage on a survey but who become very uncomfortable when their child brings home a new romantic partner of a different ethnicity: "Sure I approve of interracial marriage, just not for my son or daughter."

Protective Caution

To better understand both sides of potentially polarizing views, it is worth noting that when people have reservations about interracial couples, it is not always motivated by discriminatory disdain for persons of other ethnicities. Often, the motivation stems from a genuine concern regarding whether a person's choice to marry someone from a different ethnic background will lower their value for their own cultural heritage. Parents around the world spend years imparting their appreciation for the actions and experiences of their ancestors, and they hope that those actions and experiences will motivate future generations to promote, protect, and maintain those cultural values.

A MOTHER'S REQUEST

Consider... a freshman preparing to leave home for college. Before he leaves, he walks over to his mother, who gives him a long hug. In that hug, he feels appreciation for all that his mother has done for him. As a single mother, she worked hard to raise him to be hardworking and respectful of others. She helped form his ideas of what it means to be a man, a Black man, a good person, a faith-filled person, and a giving person. After a brief parting kiss on the cheek, his mother calmly puts her hands on both of his shoulders and says, "Now don't you marry a White woman."

Whoa! Shocked and appalled, the son looks at his mother confused. These offensive words came from the same woman who raised him to be accepting of everyone (regardless of their differences), to see value in everyone, and to speak up for those who were misunderstood, mistreated, or dismissed unjustifiably. As this young man wrestles with the apparent contradiction between this statement and the values he was raised with, he begins to realize that it wasn't as much of a contradiction after all. He realizes that his mother didn't suddenly become racist and antagonistic toward those from other ethnic backgrounds. Nor was she threatening to disown him if he brought home a White spouse to meet her. She was expressing a concern for his values and also his well-being, consistent with everything else she has taught him.

Regarding his values, she was concerned that marrying someone from a different ethnic background might feel like she was losing a soldier in the fight to preserve appreciation for their cultural heritage. She concluded that the joining of two differing cultural values would, at best, mean they would share or split their time in maintaining cultural values and traditions. At worst, she concluded that her son would let go of his cultural values and traditions altogether in favor of his partner's.

Regarding his well-being, she was concerned that if he began a relationship with someone from a different ethnic cultural background, life would become more difficult for him. He and his partner would have to endure lingering social stigmas and would continually need to defend their relationship. They would also have difficulties making and maintaining supportive friendships, and they would have limited potential to advance in their career due to their spousal choices. There might also be potential safety concerns from those who choose to express their disapproval in physically aggressive ways. Not only that, but these concerns would apply to their future children as well. What at first seemed shocking was, in fact, an expression of care.

This example highlights the delicate empathy balance required by helping professionals when they encounter individuals who express seemingly offensive messages. If these messages are based on derogatory beliefs regarding people of certain ethnicities, then the goal is to find a way to challenge those views for the well-being of the individual and everyone they encounter in the future. However, if that is not the motivation behind the message, then it's in our best interest to make the most of every opportunity to learn about the individual's true motivations—including their hopes and concerns—so we can guide them to take a healthy perspective and engage in healthy decision making. To do this, we must first resist the urge to respond prematurely based on inaccurate conclusions of prejudice.

For example, when interracial couples are wrestling with societal stigmas—as well as personal cultural identity struggles—it is not uncommon for one partner to express to another, "I love you, but we cannot take this relationship any further because we're from different worlds, and I'm not sure if our love for each other is enough to overcome the difficulties we would face. I can't bring you home to my family. What would my family say? What would my friends say? What does our relationship say about me to those within my cultural group? To those outside of my cultural group? To me?"

On the surface, these questions have the potential to seem disrespectful and to indicate unhealthy relationship priorities. They may also seem to indicate that the partner has rigid family boundaries that are unaccepting of newcomers or that their commitment to the relationship isn't secure enough to withstand outside pressures. While that might be true for some individuals, for others, these questions represent obstacles that can be overcome. As a helping professional, you can make a significant impact by taking the time to sufficiently and nonjudgmentally explore, understand, and empathize with the couple—allowing their concerns to be heard so the relationship can be pursued. Without being a cultural expert, you can explore what is important to the couple, including their hopes as well as their concerns, and help them choose a healthy path forward.

For interracial couples who have children, there are other common experiences to explore. For example, to prevent reasonable assumptions from becoming points of contention, the couple would be wise to explore as early as possible what value they place on maintaining cultural uniqueness, even as they choose how they will share cultural values together. Similarly, it would be beneficial to determine how they will choose to raise their children (e.g., what holidays they will celebrate, what traditions they will keep). Will they promote more of one partner's cultural values, promote them both equally, or promote neither so their children can decide for themselves? As helping professionals, it can be easy for us to have a strong preference for what direction we believe the couple should choose. However, to reduce the likelihood that our own cultural preferences and biases will skew our ability to provide them with support, we should focus on learning and empathizing with what the couple values and why, and then help them choose what is healthiest for them.

More Like Mom, Dad, Both, or Neither?

Multiethnic families also experience a common dilemma when it comes to how they prefer to be identified with certain terms of reference. For example, if a child's mother identifies as Chinese American and the father identifies as African American, then how will the child identify if asked about their ethnicity? For some children, it depends on the relationship they have with one or both parents. For others, it depends on the values that have been directly or indirectly instilled into them. For others still, it is a source of internal confusion that never gets resolved. These identity questions have implications not only for the child but also for the parents. Many parents from multiethnic families hope their child will identify similarly to how they identify themselves and feel hurt if the child identifies more strongly with the other parent.

When parents exhibit concerns about how their child will identify, it is not only because they want to share their child's cultural identity for bonding purposes. There are practical benefits as well. Many multiethnic parents are concerned that, when in public, someone else will mistake them for a babysitter rather than their child's parent due to differences in skin tone. The impact of this public perception is even more inconvenient if a child gets displaced in a public place. When that parent goes to retrieve their child at the lost-and-found station, they risk facing staff members who are hesitant or resistant to release the child into their care because the child's differing skin tone calls their parental status into question. It is truly a privilege when people are able to leave home with their children, and they don't have to ensure that there are family photos on their phone or in their wallet in case they have to prove to someone that their child is theirs.

The One-Drop Rule

The one-drop rule is a term that dates back to slavery times in America. In an effort to identify persons of African descent, no matter how light a person's skin tone was, if that person was found to have even one drop of African blood in them, then that was enough for them to be legally treated as African and thus enslaved. While the one-drop rule legally lasted until 1967, when it was deemed unconstitutional, the unofficial practice continues to this day.

This unofficial practice impacts multiethnic families because self-identification is a luxury that many feel like they don't have. For many multiethnic families, society conveys how the family is seen, regardless of how they see themselves. Consider the child of the Chinese American mother and African American father mentioned previously. Whether that child is raised to identify as Chinese American, African American, multiethnic, interracial, or another term of reference, this will not stop society from seeing that child as one thing, which is often based on the most observable trait: the color of their skin. Therefore, despite this child's multiethnic heritage, it is likely that in social settings, that child will simply be considered Black.

This tendency to identify people's ethnic cultural heritage by certain default observable characteristics is seen in popular society as well. For example, President Barack Obama may have had a White American mother and a Kenyan father, yet he is commonly referred to as America's first Black president. Similarly, Tiger Woods's father was of African American, Chinese, and Native American descent, while his mother is of Thai, Chinese, and Dutch descent. Although Tiger refers to himself as "Cablinasian" (to reflect an ethnic identity of Caucasian, Black, Indian, and Asian), society commonly refers to him as the best Black golfer in the world. Actor Dwayne Johnson, whose mother is Samoan and whose father is of Black Nova Scotian heritage, has joked that one reason he gets so many acting roles in Hollywood is because he is ethnically ambiguous, reflecting how he can play any role because people think he fits whatever that role is.

As helping professionals, our goal is to help as many people as we possibly can. Take the time to explore the varying experiences of multiethnic families. Identify with as many experiences as you can, and increase your understanding of and empathy for the new experiences you discover. Then use this knowledge to reassure your clients and build greater rapport with them. By providing support for those individuals and families, you are planting seeds that will impact everyone they encounter.

Use the worksheet on the next page to reflect on your own journey in supporting multiethnic families, and explore opportunities to learn more on this journey.

Cultural Competency Journey Reflection

What cultural values would I strive to maintain if I were in an interracial relationship?

_____

_____

_____

_____

What beliefs do I have about interracial relationships? What experiences do I have or have I witnessed that support those beliefs?

_____

_____

_____

_____

What opportunities do I have to learn more about multiethnic families?

_____

_____

_____

_____

Gender

When addressing the topic of gender, it is beneficial to focus on the significance of gender equality. Gender equality involves the acknowledgment that no gender wants to be considered inferior. In an attempt to avoid inferiority, many seek to promote themselves and their gender as superior. However, what people intend as an assertion of their legitimate value and worth in defense of their gender is often interpreted as an offensive expression against the legitimate value and worth of another gender. The day-to-day implications of misunderstandings such as these fuel many unhealthy interactions. As helping professionals, it is in our best interest to cultivate value for persons of any gender and to learn how to identify these misunderstandings and help repair damaged relationships.

Sexism

Sexism has been described as prejudice, stereotypes, or discrimination based on a person's gender. In American society, this has been predominately, although not exclusively, experienced by women, who have brought attention to various perceptions or practices, both unintentional and intentional, that are discriminatory in nature or impact.

An example of sexism is the gender-influenced glass ceiling in the workplace, where despite the fact that women work as hard or harder than the men around them, they continually get passed up for promotions and receive insufficient explanations for these management decisions. Job perceptions are often unequal as well. For example, a man can walk into a new management role wearing a power suit, a power stare, and a power tie, and he'll be praised for assertively declaring that his presence is a signal that things are going to change. Unfortunately, women who employ the same leadership strategy receive a colder reception and are often described as "trying too hard," which reflects the double standard present in the workplace. As a helping professional, you may be called upon to support women who feel devalued and to help them find a way to express their best selves, while also learning to cope with those who aren't ready to see this best self.

In addition to sexism in the workplace, women encounter microaggressions in the context of intimate partner violence. Here, women who have been sexually abused are often confronted with the insinuation that they provoked the abuser. Whether in courtrooms, living rooms, or therapy rooms, many people fail to see the impact of asking someone who was sexually abused, "Well, what were you wearing when it happened?" Although this question may be asked to gain a full and complete understanding of the experience, if it is the only question, or one of only a few questions asked, then it is more likely to be interpreted as an accusation. It conveys that the answer to the question might explain or justify the sexual abuse.

The #MeToo Movement is just one of the many efforts to help give voice to experiences that have been unseen and unheard for years. Similarly, the Time's Up Movement has sought to build an increased awareness of sexual harassment and to help generate concrete change, leading to safety and equity in workplace experiences. As a therapist, you may be called upon to help someone process difficult experiences of sexual abuse or gender-based inequalities. Focus on seeing the value in the person's experience of themselves, especially if their experience differs from others' experience of them. As it specifically relates to gender, take the time to learn about misunderstandings regarding people's values and abilities, and find ways to convey your empathy and desire to help them change their future experiences for the better.

Sexism and Men

Despite popular opinion to the contrary, men can experience sexism as well. This is not intended to diminish women's experiences of gender inequality but to acknowledge that alongside those experiences, men have experienced discrimination, stereotypes, and prejudices based on their gender as well.

Although men are advantaged by male privilege, that privilege is often awarded partially or conditionally, based on how closely they conform to society's expectations for their gender. Consider males in predominately female professions (e.g., male flight attendants, nurses, hairstylists) who have to justify their careers or face professional or even family ridicule and judgment. Consider also the stay-at-home fathers who frequently have to defend themselves and their choice to be the primary caregiver to their children. Consider the confused and often derogatory looks men get when they ask their employer whether the company provides paternity leave, only to be asked, "What's that?" or "Is that a thing?" or "Why do *you* need to be at home?"—as if it only matters if a newborn child develops a close bond with their mother.

THE STAY-AT-HOME HUSBAND STIGMA

Consider... a man who expressed frustration at how often he had to assert that he was not taking advantage of his wife by staying home with the children. This man and his wife were both gainfully employed in fast-moving careers. As they explored expanding their family, they realized the unfortunate reality that if she left the workforce for any length of time to be a mother, when she returned, she would likely have to start a bit behind and catch up in order to thrive. However, because of the gender inequalities at work, the husband would not face this same challenge. As a result, they both decided that the wife would continue working full time and become the primary earner while the father would transition to a full-time parent. These considerations were influenced by a value for full-time parental care, not the gendered stereotypes that the husband was lazy and not a "real" man.

As helping professionals, we have the challenge of understanding gendered stereotypes and supportively challenging them so we can help clients develop healthier relationships. It also allows us to better protect and advocate for those who have been negatively impacted by these stereotypes.

Men and Sexual Abuse

In addition to the common misperception that gender discrimination doesn't apply to men, many people also believe that sexual abuse doesn't apply to men. This misguided belief unfortunately contributes to the minimization of men's abuse experiences, which can have as devastating of effects on men as they have had for women in similar circumstances.

Many who have difficulty accepting this reality cite the history of male-dominated societal patterns and the unequal role of power held by men. However, one need not argue against this reality to address the coinciding reality that there are circumstances in which men also feel powerless and are subjected to abusive situations. For example, while many men experience domestic abuse (including physical, emotional, and verbal abuse), they often feel powerless to change their situation because domestic abuse resources often exclude men, isolated when their feelings are often invalidated by others because of their maleness, and emotionally paralyzed by internal feelings of shame influenced by beliefs that "a real man wouldn't let this happen to them."

Even still, some point to anatomical differences between men and women and argue that any sexual encounters with men would naturally be consensual because if the man wasn't interested, he would not be physically aroused in order for a sexual encounter to occur. However, this argument fails to differentiate between an involuntary bodily reaction and voluntary consent. It also assumes that a particular type of sexual activity occurred, when in reality sexual abuse can take many different forms.

For example, consider a man who is incarcerated and expresses to you that he was taken advantage of by a cellmate who forced him to do things he didn't want to do. He feared for his physical well-being if he didn't oblige. He also believed that those in authority would not advocate for him because they continually stated that whatever happened behind bars was not their concern and was a natural consequence for the actions that got him incarcerated in the first place. Although there are thousands of people wrongfully convicted of serious crimes each year (Zalman, 2012), the cause of their incarceration is not a justification for sexual abuse. As helping professionals, it is essential that we see the devastating impact of these experiences on a person's sense of self, their gender and sexual identity, and their overall sense of agency and ability to control what happens to them in this world.

As another example, consider a man who shares with you that he was a victim of incest, having been taken advantage of by an older family member when he was younger. Incest is particularly difficult to process and move on from because it often involves a family member who was previously trusted and deemed safe. It can have a long-term impact on victims and influence their views of themselves, as well as their ability to trust others. Significant others often struggle with how to support their partner in consideration of this discovered sexual abuse history. You don't need to have all of the answers or shared experiences to be able to give validity to the gravity of the experience. You can still give legitimacy to how difficult it will be to process the impact of the abuse on their lives and help them move forward in a healthy way.

Finally, consider a young man who accepted an invitation to his first college party and who, after staying to himself most of the night, woke up to find himself in an unknown bed, with an unknown woman. Although he made intentional efforts to behave responsibly and avoid trouble, he was unaware that someone had slipped a substance into his nonalcoholic drink. When tells his friends how distraught he is, he receives playful sarcasm about how painful it must have been to wake up next to a gorgeous woman. What they don't understand is the internal struggle this young man faces as he not only tries to process his own feelings, but also worries about how to tell his girlfriend: his high school sweetheart, whom he hopes to marry and to whom he hoped to lose his virginity.

Desiring to tell the most important person in his life something that would surely devastate her, this young man also struggles with what the incident says about him. Is he no longer a virgin? Does it count if he was unconscious when it happened? After he tells his girlfriend, she wrestles with similar dilemmas, and they seek the support and guidance of a counselor, where his girlfriend sincerely says, "I was raised to believe that 'once a cheater, always a cheater,' so does this mean he's a cheater?" The boyfriend—genuinely curious—chimes in as well by asking, "Yeah, does this mean I'm a cheater?" Unfortunately, the counselor responds, "Well, you see, it's different with men. Even though you were unconscious, the fact that you allowed it to happen suggests that there is a subconscious issue of fidelity that needs to be addressed."

Now this young man not only feels confused about what happened and why, but he is also beating himself up because he believes that a trustworthy, faithful, and committed partner would have been strong enough to avoid this scenario regardless of consciousness. Helping professionals seeking to support couples in situations like these need to be able to see the legitimate impact this has on both partners while withholding their own judgments and presumptions. They also need to acknowledge that regardless of fault, the ramifications of the event may have long-lasting effects—all while taking care to avoid minimizing the man's experience by concluding that he simply must have subconsciously wanted it to happen.

These are just a few examples of how sexist and gender-influenced stereotypes can negatively impact our interactions with others. And while there are definitely differences between genders in their experience of discrimination, there are also similarities that make everyone's experience valid and worthy of being heard.

Use the worksheet on the next page to reflect on how you can make the most of opportunities to expand your perspective on gender discrimination, regardless of the client's gender, and practice empathy and support.

Cultural Competency Journey Reflection

Have I ever felt discriminated against based on my gender?

_____

_____

_____

Have I ever felt uncomfortable sharing about an experience where I was treated unfairly based on my gender?

_____

_____

_____

How can I reassure others that I am a safe person to talk to if they feel they have been treated unfairly based on their gender?

_____

_____

_____

How can I be an advocate for those who have experienced gender discrimination?

_____

_____

_____

Sexual Orientation & Gender Identity

Gender identity and sexual orientation are frequent sources of discrimination in our society. This is especially so for those who identify as part of the LGBTQ+ community. In order to be effective as helping professionals and to support the greatest variety of clients possible, we need to increase our understanding of not only our own gender identity and sexual orientation but also those of individuals who are similar to *and* different from us.

In an ongoing effort to increase cultural competence regarding gender identity and sexual orientation, let's elaborate on the commonly used term of reference: LGBTQ+. As awareness of the experiences of those in this community increases, so does the vocabulary used to assist in healthy communication and understanding. Accordingly, convenient acronyms like LGBT grow to become LGBTQ, then LGBTQIA, then LGBTQ$_2$IA, and so on. After a while, the term LGBTQ+ became popularized to convey that it is not about a finite number of exhaustive and absolute terms but, rather, a community of individuals seeking to be understood and accepted in their various expressions and identities.

To increase understanding and empathy for the many experiences and concerns of this community, let's briefly explore the acronym LGBTQ$_2$IA. To assist in this effort, I will refer to a 2021 glossary of terms provided by PFLAG, the first and largest organization for lesbian, gay, bisexual, transgender, and queer (LGBTQ+) people, their parents and families, and allies. To get us started on this journey, consider the following vignette.

PRIDE PARADE T-SHIRTS

Consider... a pride parade that provides a significant opportunity for those in the LGBTQ+ community to celebrate their identity, self-acceptance, and social achievements. At the beginning of the parade route, there lay piles of plain brown boxes, filled with plain white

T-shirts, each emblazoned with a single word in black letters displayed across the front. As people prepare to enter the parade, each individual selects and puts on the shirt that best represents them.

If it is not clear by now, this is a completely hypothetical depiction of a pride parade—as a pride parade simply filled with plain white T-shirts would be a boring parade by anyone's standards. However, I share this analogy as a helpful visual while increasing your understanding of the individuals who might identify with various parade T-shirts. Let's take a look at some of the available T-shirts:

> **Lesbian:**
> A woman who is emotionally, romantically, and/or physically attracted to other women.

> **Gay:**
> A person who is emotionally, romantically, and/or physically attracted to people of the same gender.

Although *lesbian* is often a preferred term for women, many women also use the term *gay* to describe themselves. However, it does not work the other way around in that men do not identify as lesbian.

> **Bisexual:**
> A person who has the capacity for attraction—emotionally, romantically, and/or physically—to people of more than one gender.

Note that despite its prefix, the term *bisexual* does not necessarily mean that a person is only attracted to the two binary genders (men and women), or that they are exclusionary towards nonbinary people (defined next). For some bisexual people, the *bi* refers to genders similar to and genders different from their own. Other people prefer the term *pansexual*, which is a similar but distinct identity that reflects attraction to people inclusive of all genders.

> **Transgender:**
> A person whose gender identity differs from conventional expectations based on their assigned sex at birth (often shortened to *trans*). **Transsexual** is a term that is less frequently used and commonly misunderstood—with some finding it offensive or outdated and others believing it uniquely applies to them—that refers to a person who uses medical interventions, such as hormone therapy or gender-affirming surgeries, as a part of a process of expressing their gender. Many are averse to the term *transsexual* because it can be misinterpreted as referencing sexuality rather than gender identity. **Cisgender** refers to a person whose gender identity matches the sex they were assigned at birth. **Nonbinary** often falls under the transgender umbrella and refers to individuals who identify as neither man nor woman, as both man and woman, or as a combination of man or woman.

There is an online graphic that depicts being transgender better than any simplified language I can offer. In the picture, you see the back of a shirtless woman with long hair flowing down her back, and she's wearing denim jeans and a belt. You see her staring into a full-length mirror, and in the reflection, she sees staring back at her a shirtless man with short hair, wearing denim jeans and a belt. This graphic depicts the reality that transgender individuals face: The gender they see on the outside does not reflect the gender they know they are.

To assist you in your efforts to empathize with and understand the experience of trans individuals, imagine you are unwittingly on an episode of *The Twilight Zone*. In this episode, you—as you are now, without changing a single aspect of your identity or a single day of your personal history—wake up tomorrow morning, and in looking in the mirror, you see a person who looks similar to you but is of a different gender. Outside of the initial shock and confusion, odds are good that you wouldn't all of a sudden change your understanding of your identity. Rather, you'd see yourself as someone who is one gender on the inside but who is, for some reason, trapped in the body of a different gender. While not every trans person would describe their experience in this exact way—some, for example, feel comfortable with their body but do not identify as the gender that other people assign to their body—if you can imagine yourself in this experience, you will at least be headed in the direction of increased understanding and empathy for those who have similar experiences in their real lives.

So far, in our exploration of the acronym LGBTQ$_2$IA, we have addressed L, G, B, and T, representing lesbian, gay, bisexual, and transgender. The Q$_2$ that follows represents two Qs, so let's continue exploring what the remaining letters in the acronym represent.

> **Queer:**
> A term used by some LGBTQ+ people to describe themselves and/or their community.

PFLAG goes on to explain that *queer* has traditionally been a negative or pejorative term for people who are gay, so the term is still sometimes disliked within the LGBTQ+ community. Due to its varying meanings, PFLAG recommends that *queer* only be used when self-identifying or quoting someone who self-identifies as queer (e.g., "My cousin identifies as genderqueer").

Questioning:
A person who is in the process of discovery and exploration about their sexual orientation, gender identity, gender expression, or a combination thereof.

It is important to understand that questioning can occur at any stage in life. It is not synonymous with being confused. It is not simply a process of choosing one's preferred terminology for one's gender or sexual orientation. To help increase understanding and empathy, consider the following continuation of the pride parade analogy.

A PRIDE PARADE DILEMMA

Consider... the pride parade with its box of plain white T-shirts displaying single words. As the crowd around the boxes disperses, we see an individual standing over the boxes.

We take a peek inside this person's thoughts and hear what they have discovered about their identity and what has yet to be discovered. This person knows that a cisgender, heterosexual identity doesn't seem to fit them, but they have not yet found a descriptive label that does fit. No single word seems to perfectly describe what has, thus far, only been an internal and evolving understanding of their identity. This individual is unsure where all this internal processing will ultimately lead to. Then the *questioning* T-shirt comes into view, and the individual selects this shirt to wear, proudly displaying it down the parade walk.

As a helping professional, you may be called upon to help a person questioning their sexual orientation or gender identity. In such an opportunity, you are not responsible for telling them the "right" answer or for helping them choose from available options. Rather, you have the challenge of nonjudgmentally helping them understand themselves as they already are. Whatever labels apply at the end of that self-exploration process are secondary.

Intersex:

A person who is biologically between the medical definitions of male and female, which can be through variations in hormones, chromosomes, internal or external genitalia, or any primary and/or secondary sex characteristics. Medical professionals often assign a gender to an intersex individual at birth and perform surgeries to "align" their physical appearance with typical male or female sex characteristics to conform to societal and binary expectations (rather than to alleviate an actual health issue), a practice that is opposed by PFLAG, the Intersex Society of North America, and others who advocate for the well-being of intersex people. Intersex replaces the outdated, and now offensive, term *hermaphrodite*.

Intersex people are more common than society acknowledges; you just don't see them. Because intersex individuals do not fit within society's binary norm, there are legitimate fears and experiences of discrimination that hinder freedom of expression and that prevent people from having the healthy conversations needed to increase understanding and reduce stigma.

Many helping professionals will express that while they are sympathetic to this experience, they feel like they don't need to invest time in increasing their knowledge, understanding, and empathy for intersex individuals because they are such a small portion of the population. While the likelihood that you will work with someone who is intersex is admittedly statistically slim, there is still the potential for damage to occur—both to the client-professional relationship and to the client's sense of self—if the situation is not handled professionally. Therefore, it is nonetheless beneficial to increase your cultural competence in this area.

AN INTERSEX DILEMMA

Consider... a therapist and a client who, after spending several months working through some significant struggles with depression and anxiety, are discussing the end of their professional relationship due to significant progress the client has made. During the session, the client expresses some hesitancy with terminating therapy due to a remaining concern. The client says, "Remember when we first began and I expressed that I had two primary struggles I needed help with—depression and anxiety? What I didn't mention is there was a third struggle. I usually keep that one to myself because I can't trust everyone with it. The few times I have risked sharing it, it resulted in irreversible tension, discomfort, and sometimes the loss of relationships altogether. I feel like I can risk trusting you with it and that you might be able to help me reduce that internal struggle. My boyfriend and I are at a point where I'd like to start being sexually intimate together, but I'm worried about how he'll react when I explain something about my body to him. I was born with intersex, and while people have always seen me as female and I identify as a woman, I do have some physical characteristics that make me different from most women.

After hearing all of this, the therapist gently responds, "I'm sorry, I'd love to help, but I don't believe in that." Confused, the client asks, "I don't understand. You don't believe in what? The type of body I have?"

This therapist had difficulty separating the client's physiological reality from the therapist's own personal, spiritual, or political beliefs about sexual orientation and gender identity. Regardless of our own beliefs, we as helping professionals need to be able to meet people where they are at, making them feel understood and accepted as people. We must help them cope with life's challenges and make healthy decisions for the best life possible. Increasing your cultural competence and overall understanding of a greater variety of diverse life experiences can significantly aid in these efforts by improving the quality of your relationships, as well as the efficacy of your helping efforts.

Asexual:
A person who does not experience sexual attraction.

As we move on to the A in LGBTQ$_2$IA, it is important to note that the term *asexual* does not refer to a person who has simply chosen not to engage in sexual activity with anyone or just not found a partner they are sufficiently attracted to. Asexual describes a person who does not experience sexual feelings in general. For some helping professionals, increasing their empathy for asexuality is so outside of their personal experience that it is akin to trying to understand how a person could never experience hunger for food. If a person is asexual, it doesn't necessarily mean they have never participated in a sexual encounter but, rather, that it wasn't preceded by the same physical desire, or meet the same need, that is associated with sexual attraction.

> **Ally:**
> A person who is supportive of LGBTQ+ individuals
> and the community, either personally or as an advocate.

Although the A in LGBTQ$_2$IA is often associated with asexual, it is also associated with *ally*. Allies can be heterosexual and cisgender people who advocate for equality in partnership with LGBTQ+ people. Sometimes allies have a close family member or friend who has helped them gain an appreciation for the struggles experienced by the community, and the ally desires to be a part of reducing those struggles (e.g., by standing against social injustices) and increasing the quality of and value for life of those in the LGBTQ+ community. The term *ally* also refers to individuals who are LGBTQ+ and who are supportive of other identities within the community.

A SURPRISE ALLY

Consider… a man who grabs an ally T-shirt at the beginning of the parade and joins in the celebration. As he walks down the street, he spots a coworker among the crowd. They greet each other and the coworker says in surprise, "Hey John, great to see you! I didn't expect to see you here, and especially not in the parade. Aren't you married?"

"I am," John replies.

Confused, the coworker adds, "To a woman?"

"Yep!" John replies.

"And you have kids?"

Seeing the coworker's genuine desire to understand, John explains, "I am indeed a heterosexual, cisgender man, as well as a husband and a father. I also have a brother who is trans who has helped increase my awareness and understanding in many ways. I realized that watching the fight from the sidelines didn't feel right for me. I am in this fight right alongside my brother and the entire LGBTQ+ community."

Whether or not you consider yourself an ally, you can make intentional efforts to increase your understanding of the various experiences of those in the LGBTQ+ community and identify what role you can play in helping someone in that community who seeks your services and support. You don't have to put a stamp of approval on every aspect of someone's life to help them improve their life in some way.

It's Not a Phase

Two of the most commonly expressed beliefs about sexual orientation and gender identity are "It's simply a phase" and "It's a choice." People often repeat these statements as if they are facts, but they underestimate how invalidating they can be. It is interesting that so many people find it easy to conclude that sexual orientation and gender identity are lifestyle choices, yet they don't consider their heterosexuality or cisgender identity to be a lifestyle choice.

That's Not My Specialty

Another common perspective held by helping professionals is that efforts to help sexual and gender minorities should be left to the experts in those life experiences. On the one hand, specialized knowledge can be very beneficial, and there are many helping professionals who can provide perspectives and services others simply cannot. On the other hand, expert services are not always needed. Sometimes all people need is a culturally competent helping professional who knows enough to continually learn about themselves and others and who can empathize with and accept others' needs.

Still, many helping professionals assert that they will embark upon this new learning if and when there is an immediate need to do so because no one on their current client caseload identifies as LGBTQ+. This is an interesting argument when you consider that 5.6 percent of American adults identify themselves as being a part of the LGBTQ+ community (Jones, 2021). Statistically speaking, odds are that 5.6 percent of your caseload is LGBTQ+. The question is whether or not you have cultivated a safe place for clients to share that aspect of their identity. Let's make sure that, whether we know up front or not, we as helping professionals are cultivating safe places for self-expression and reasonable expectations for empathy.

Many of you reading this section may be wrestling with how to support clients who challenge your personal faith beliefs. My intended purpose in encouraging you to empathize with these clients is not to change your beliefs. It is to prepare you to respond with respect and acceptance for people regardless of potential differences in your beliefs.

THE UNNECESSARY REFERRAL

Consider… a life coach who takes on a new client. After six sessions and successful progress toward goals, the client mentions that their partner will be picking them up after the session ends. Caught off guard by the language choice, the life coach asks, "Wait, are you gay? Oh, sorry. I wish you would have told me that up front. You see, I don't specialize in working with individuals in the LGBTQ+ community. I'd be happy to refer you to a life coach who does so you can get the best possible support possible."

The client reassuringly responds, "Oh, thanks for the offer, but I'm good. That may not be your specialty, but that is also not my problem. I'm actually pretty good in that area of my life—no identity struggles, no discrimination issues I can't handle on my own. In fact, you've actually helped me make more growth in the past six weeks than any of the other life coaches I've seen previously. As long as you feel like you can continue to help me despite our differences, then I'd prefer to continue with you."

As helping professionals, we need to make sure we balance owning our own beliefs and values without imposing those beliefs and values on our clients. In addition, we need to critically assess when those beliefs and values are relevant strengths or deal breakers, and when they are unrelated to our ability to help our clients.

Although there may be legitimate differences between your experiences and those of your clients, people in the LGBTQ+ community still value it when you make efforts to genuinely empathize with their struggles and experiences—especially because it is often in contrast to the lack of understanding, empathy, and acceptance they receive in their daily lives. Remember, empathy is not about approving someone's behaviors, beliefs, or identity as right or wrong. It's about respecting and valuing people enough to be willing to learn about them and to help them improve their lives in one way or another.

Navigating Law & Politics with Sexuality & Gender

When topics surrounding sexuality and gender are in the news, they often pertain to two different groups of people: (1) one group who is defending their right to be respected and accepted for who they are and (2) another group defending their right to maintain their faith beliefs and other values. The assumption behind many of these polarized debates is that a person's sexuality and identity are a threat to other people's personal beliefs and values.

Take the battle for the legalization of same-sex marriage that went on for years, where it was legalized in many states and then revoked multiple times. Many people who voted against the legalization of same-sex marriage argued that they felt compelled to do so because they believed the LGBTQ+ community was trying to redefine their heterosexual marriage. However, individuals in the LGBTQ+ community were not fighting for the right to redefine anyone else's relationship. They were fighting to have the same legitimate rights as heterosexual couples. Therefore, if there is going to be an argument or debate when it comes to gender and sexuality, let the focus be on what the LGBTQ+ community is actually pursuing as opposed to what it is that people fear they are pursuing.

Use the following worksheet to help you explore how you can better support and understand individuals who identify as members of the LGBTQ+ community.

Cultural Competency
Journey Reflection

What aspects of the LGBTQ+ community do I need to learn most about?

_____

_____

_____

_____

In what ways can I be more supportive of those in the LGBTQ+ community?

_____

_____

_____

_____

How might I communicate my acceptance of others even when we hold potentially different values?

_____

_____

_____

_____

Persons with Disabilities

According to the U.S. Census Bureau, approximately 19 percent of the U.S. population identifies as having some form of disability (Brault, 2012). Beyond being confined to a wheelchair, disabilities can manifest both physically and mentally, impacting various aspects of daily life, including walking, speaking, seeing, hearing, learning, thinking, concentrating, working, and more. It can also include individuals with an alcohol or substance use disorder, as well those who are in recovery. In our efforts to increase our cultural competence so as to be prepared to help meet the needs of the greatest variety of clients possible, we need to increase our understanding of the experiences, strengths, and struggles of persons with disabilities.

Avoid Making Minimizing or Patronizing Assumptions

People with disabilities often admit to feeling frustrated when others incorrectly assume they know everything about a person because they know about their disability. Not only is this negative and minimizing, but it also serves as an excuse for people to no longer learn anything else about the person with the disability—as if the disability is all they need to know. While these misunderstandings are sometimes a reasonable sign of genuine ignorance, people with disabilities often find the experience to be patronizing and condescending. This is evident in the all-too-common example of someone approaching a person in a wheelchair and stating very loudly, "IS THERE ANYTHING I CAN DO TO HELP YOU?" The person in the wheelchair is likely to respond, "My legs don't work, but my hearing is fine. So please stop yelling at me!" As helping professionals, we have the opportunity to learn so we do not perpetuate these condescending experiences.

Focus on Abilities, Not Limitations

In an attempt to avoid the common tendency to minimize, patronize, or ignore persons with disabilities, some people have promoted a different way to think about disabilities altogether wherein the focus is on abilities, not limitations. In particular, people with this perspective acknowledge that there are practical inconveniences associated with disabilities, but they put more of an intentional focus on the *benefits* of that person's experience. With this perspective, a person can choose to view their disability not as a source of depression and inconvenience but, instead, as an opportunity to see and experience things others don't. For example, many people with disabilities have become motivational speakers and creative entrepreneurs by identifying and meeting needs in ways that others have not. Although it is unrealistic to expect that every person with a disability will overcome their struggles to become a motivational speaker, it seems reasonable to begin with a goal that involves focusing less on limitations and building on that progress to identify strengths and abilities.

The Value of Being Seen

One of the most common frustrations that individuals with disabilities experience is that they often feel seen but dismissed—or unseen altogether. For example, individuals confined to wheelchairs often express that people literally look over them and fail to see what they have to contribute. As a helping professional, you have the challenge to be culturally competent by showing respect and by demonstrating a willingness to provide clients with a more positive or corrective experience whenever possible. This might include taking actions that are not required but that you choose to do out of consideration for people with disabilities. For example, a health clinic might add a wheelchair ramp or designated parking spaces for individuals with disabilities. Similarly, a leadership team planning an offsite event might consider whether that site is accessible for people with disabilities and then make accommodations as necessary (e.g., ensuring the presence of sign language interpreters, the use of visual aids, and special seating for the visually impaired).

The Value of Independence

Another common misunderstanding about people with disabilities is that they like the special attention they receive (e.g., designated parking spots, front-of-the-line access and designated seating at events). Some people even make statements such as "It must be nice to get pushed around everywhere you want to go." While this perspective might make sense to the person without the disability—who is at the end of the line waiting to get in the venue or at the back of the event struggling to see—it overlooks the reality that the temporary benefits of accommodations like these pale in comparison to the 24/7 inconvenience of not having full control of one's body. In response to statements such as these, one individual with a physical disability expressed, "I would rather watch the concert from the last row of the theater if it meant I could have full use of my legs every day afterward."

RATIONED REQUESTS FOR SUPPORT

Consider... a woman struggling with a form of multiple sclerosis that results in periodic bouts of loss of feeling or debilitating pain at unpredictable times. One evening, she is at a community event she often attends. As the event concludes and the crowd departs, one gentleman notices that this woman is sitting in her car making no apparent effort to drive off. He inquires as to whether she needs help. She gives a small smile and reassures him that she is fine and will drive off soon. Satisfied by her answer, the man walks back to his car and drives home.

Unfortunately, the woman isn't fine. She is feeling increasing pain. She hoped she could get to her car and drive home before the pain worsened, but she is now unable to drive due to overwhelming pain that prevents her from operating the car. Not knowing how long the pain will last, she eventually falls asleep in the driver's seat. She wakes up several hours later to find that her pain has decreased enough for her to drive herself home safely.

The next morning, a friend checks in with her and learns about the woman's long night. Saddened by the knowledge that her friend was in pain, she asks, "Why didn't you call me? I would have come back and driven you home." Genuinely appreciating the comment, the woman replies, "I know, and that means a lot to me. But I already feel like I ask too much of you. I consider you a close friend, and while I appreciate your help, I never want you to feel like I'm using you. I'm afraid that if I ask for or accept help too often, people will get tired of offering to help. I'd rather be uncomfortable now than really need it later and have run out of support."

How difficult it must be for this woman, and many like her, to feel like she has to ration her requests for support, not knowing when she will make others feel used or taken for granted. Clients with disabilities deal with the psychological impact of having to decide how much pain and inconvenience they can endure before asking for help. And if clients don't ask for help, they risk causing a relational rupture if a family member, friend, or loved takes it personally and concludes that the client's lack of willingness to ask for help (or to accept offered help) is really a sign of lack of trust or closeness between them.

In addition to struggling with their need to depend on others, individuals with disabilities often long for a healthy sense of independence. It is incorrect to conclude that when people don't ask for help when needed, it's always out of pride. While this is sometimes true, a person may legitimately be willing to inconvenience themselves to feel a sense of independence in their ability to care for themselves—especially when they have to depend on others in so many other aspects of their lives.

Help Prevent Caregiver Burnout

For individuals who need full-time care and who have little independence, it is important to also cultivate understanding and empathy for their caregivers, who commit significant portions of their lives to investing in the care of someone else. These caregivers are dedicated to providing services that can't be accomplished alone. While caregiving can be emotionally fulfilling—given that someone gets to be a part of improving the quality of life of another person—it can also be physically and emotionally draining. Many parents genuinely love their children and still find themselves exhausted when they need to care for them 24/7 without the assistance of school, after-school activities, or camps during summer breaks. However, caregivers are often ignored and viewed as a living piece of equipment whose only meaning in life is the service they provide.

If you have a client with a full-time caregiver, you have the opportunity to strengthen the client-caregiver relationship by intentionally acknowledging and valuing the caregiver during your interactions. If the caregiver's relationship with the client is not strong, you can model appreciation of their efforts to assist in strengthening that relationship. And even if the relationship is strong, you might be the only person in the caregiver's daily interactions to provide such a gift. If you've never been in a caregiving role, take the time to imagine yourself in the caregiver's position, to learn more about their experiences (the highs and the lows), and to show empathy along the way. Just letting them know they are seen and valued goes a long way.

Invisible Disabilities

While accommodating physical and other visible disabilities is a great place to start, we must also make intentional efforts to consider the impact of invisible disabilities and to make accommodations that can benefit these individuals.

"BUT YOU DON'T LOOK DISABLED"

Consider... an aspiring helping professional who, after years of work to overcome a learning disability with reading, has obtained an advanced degree and has just taken the licensure exam in his field. The joy of this culmination of hard work is depleted upon discovering he has failed the exam.

At first, he experiences feelings of failure, followed by confusion over his test preparedness. He then starts to wonder whether he has chosen the appropriate career path. After the initial shock wears off, he is reminded of his history of test-taking struggles. When he was in school, courses that required a lot of reading and testing were more difficult to pass than courses with papers and projects.

Although he went through a majority of his educational career determined to not ask for accommodations, the failure to pass this exam forces him to acknowledge his learning disability and apply for testing accommodations, which include a private room with a desk (to reduce visual stimulation), headphones (to reduce auditory stimulation), and extra time to complete the test (in case the stimuli reduction is not sufficient). The next time he takes the test, he passes. He feels validated knowing he didn't fail the test the first time because of insufficient intelligence.

In addition to the internal struggles that individuals with invisible disabilities wrestle with, they also often experience external resistance from service providers who refuse to accept their requests for accommodations. Many providers mistakenly assume that the disability must be fake because they cannot physically see the person's limitations. This often requires individuals with disabilities to get additional professionals to verify the disability before they will be taken seriously. Other times, the opposition is more social. For example, the young man in the previous example might encounter a fellow test taker who derisively expresses, "If he gets to have more time for his exam, then I should be able to have more time for mine. It's stressful for me too." While test stress is significant for many of us, it can be minimizing to equate momentary test stress with a lifelong internal struggle and disability that has taken years of strategic effort to cope with for daily functioning.

As a helping professional, you may have the opportunity to hold a decision-making role regarding the accommodations of others or to advocate for the legitimacy of someone else's need for accommodations. In these roles, you have the chance to shape how people see their areas of strength and growth. It is essential that we see people for who they are, beyond the sum of their abilities or disabilities.

A BODY BETRAYED

Consider... an experience I had that changed my life forever. Several years ago, when my wife and I lived in California, we traveled to the Midwest to celebrate Thanksgiving with my family. We had a great time, ate great food, and had quality family time.

Late Thanksgiving night, I ended up severely dehydrated and was rushed to the hospital. After a long emergency room experience, I was diagnosed with the stomach flu and given fluids and anti-nausea medicine. For most of Friday, I rested, with the hope that if I took care of myself and had an uneventful Friday and Saturday, I'd be well enough to keep our flight back to California on Sunday. Friday and Saturday went well. On Sunday, we arrived at the airport with ample time to relax at the terminal gate as we patiently waited for our flight to board and depart.

As we waited, I began to feel uncomfortable, feeling a tightness and curling in my right toes that made me try to flex and stretch them back and forth to find relief. The tight feeling began to extend to the ball of my right foot and ankle, compelling me to press and release them against the ground as if squashing a bug. When that didn't work, and knowing we had time to spare, I told my wife I was feeling a bit of muscle tension and needed to walk it off. So off I went, slowly walking, flexing my toes, pressing my feet, and twisting my legs for added benefit. Not only did it not help, but it got worse. I awkwardly tried to keep my balance as my toes, feet, and entire right leg gradually turned further inward, twisting painfully as if trying to remove excess water from a wet towel.

Beginning to get really concerned, I turned around and headed back to our gate. I then began to feel a similar tightness in the fingers on my right hand, and my fingers started to curl, followed by my right wrist and elbow, securing itself tightly to my chest as it tried to rotate inward without ceasing. I sped up my hobbled walk as much as I could in that condition, but then my neck began to turn my head to the left without my permission and beyond the point of comfort. At that point, I was desperately using my left hand to pull my head back in the other direction in order to reduce the pain and oppose the inward force trying to turn my head.

Eventually, I reached my wife, and when she looked up and saw the condition I was in, I could see the shock and confusion on her face as she asked, "What happened to you?!" I responded with an uncharacteristically panicked and painful, "I don't know, but it hurts. I can't go another couple of hours like this on the plane. I think I need some help." My wife went to the ticket counter and sought help. Our tickets were canceled, and I was transported directly from the airport gate to the closest emergency room.

During my time in the emergency room, I contemplated several things. What was going on? How long would it last? Would I be able to take care of myself, or would I need assistance to accomplish anything for the remainder of my life? Was my career of helping others going to become a thing of the past? Although my body was not under my control, my mind was unaffected—but would people give me the time of day if I looked like this when they first met me? Would my life be filled with people giving me patronizing looks because they would assume that my physical limitations were synonymous with mental limitations?

As a husband, I wondered how my wife was doing. One moment, she was married to a husband with no disabilities, and the next, she was potentially a full-time caregiver. How stressful must that have been? How much of her life would she have to give up? We had considered having children, but was that off the table now?

The emergency room experience turned hopeful when the doctor explained that the anti-nausea medication I was prescribed a few nights earlier to treat stomach flu is in a class of medicines that contain an ingredient I am allergic to. Years later, there remains a laminated card in my wallet that I can wordlessly provide to emergency medical professionals that instructs them not to give me any medication from this class of drugs again. Hopefully, I will never have to use that card or endure an experience like that again.

Whenever I think about that day, I experience conflicted emotions. While I never want to relive such a traumatic experience—and I am immensely grateful that it only lasted several hours rather than the rest of my life—it allowed me to feel significantly more empathy for those who experience various disabilities every day of their lives. They don't have the luxury of experiencing relief after a few hours. For them, it is a continual internal and external challenge. As a counselor, I find myself compelled to be more intentional about conveying value and respect to persons with disabilities, not only because it's a good gift to offer anyone but because it increases the likelihood that I can be a source of strength and encouragement for someone who is rarely seen or valued by society. In addition, I feel compelled to utilize my experience to increase my ability to serve others by offering them an uncommon experience of empathy.

THE PERSON BEYOND THE DISABILITY

Consider... an initial meeting I had with a new adolescent client for in-home counseling services. As I approached the home, I noticed a wheelchair ramp and was curious to find out who in the home required it. When the door opened, I was greeted by the adolescent's mother, who had a type of cerebral palsy that contributed to limited body and facial mobility, communication challenges, and confinement to a wheelchair.

As I gained the adolescent's trust, I learned that part of her struggles with self-esteem and emotion regulation involved her frustration that her mother wasn't "like other mothers" or the ideal mother she dreamed she would have. She loved her mother, and she felt bad for even feeling a sense of loss considering all of the efforts her mother put forth on her behalf. As I gained trust with my client's mother, I learned that she was very empathic of her daughter's struggles and wanted to do whatever was within her power to provide as close to a normal life as possible. Over time, my client and her mother were able to share their feelings with each other, and their relationship improved.

On my last day in their home, my client's mother asked for a brief moment alone, where she shared that she appreciated my efforts at improving her relationship with her daughter and also appreciated my respectful and considerate interactions with her. She added that in her efforts to support her daughter, she had to navigate various service representatives, many of whom dismissed her altogether, continually implying that she was unable to make decisions—as if her physical disability reduced her competency. However, she expressed that since the first day, I looked her in the eyes, patiently listened as she forced her mouth to communicate the words she wanted to convey, and treated her words and perspective with value. She stated that she felt that I saw her beyond her disability, which she not only appreciated, but she believed served as a model for her daughter in a way no one had done for her before.

While I was serving this family, I wasn't on any disability advocacy campaign. I was simply fulfilling my professional commitment to improve the quality of life of others in whatever way I could. However, I realize that if I hadn't gone through my traumatic airport experience, I might not have been so supportive. My experience allowed me to view my client's mom as an intelligent and capable person, as someone with feelings and emotions who deserved the same respect, value, and consideration as everyone else. So, while I acknowledged the reality of the disability, I chose to value and speak to the person beyond the disability.

I don't know what experiences you have had in your lifetime, but I encourage you to explore them and to discover what you may have gone through that can increase your capacity to understand the experiences of others.

The reflection questions on the next page can assist you in this exploration. I also encourage you to learn from my experience and to be similarly compelled to see the person beyond the disability. Make intentional efforts to see that **a person is more than the sum of their disabilities;** you might be pleasantly surprised by whom you find.

Cultural Competency Journey Reflection

In what ways can I improve the quality of my interactions with persons with disabilities?

_____

_____

_____

_____

In what ways can I be more supportive of persons with disabilities (e.g., providing or advocating for accommodations)?

_____

_____

_____

_____

What opportunities do I currently have to learn more about and empathize with the experiences of those with disabilities?

_____

_____

_____

_____

Language & Interpreters

As helping professionals working in a continually more diverse world, you will likely encounter clients who either they themselves, or their family and loved ones, speak English as a second language or speak no English at all. Language has the potential to be a significant part of a person's cultural self-identity, and it is one of the many ways we may differ from those we serve. Therefore, to increase cultural competence with regard to language, we must learn to be less inconvenienced by language differences. Instead, we can look at other languages as an opportunity to understand and interact with a greater variety of people. Let's explore a few considerations that can reduce the potential impact of language barriers on the effectiveness of your professional efforts.

Resist the Guilt of Not Knowing Other Languages

Well-meaning helping professionals often minimize their ability to serve individuals and families who do not speak English. Some go so far as to feel guilty for not knowing other languages, as if to convey that a true professional would have learned more languages to reduce such a barrier. However, knowing every conceivable language is an unreasonable goal given the variety of languages spoken in this country (including non-spoken languages such as American Sign Language and braille). Because you never know who might seek out your services, it's unreasonable to expect yourself to be infinitely prepared.

There are, however, times when there may be one prominent second language in your geographic area. In these situations, it may be beneficial to invest the time and energy to learn that particular language if you plan to use that language professionally.

Value the Benefits of Trained Interpreters

As a culturally competent helping professional, you don't have to allow a lack of fluency in other languages to be an absolute barrier to the provision of beneficial services. In some cases, it can be beneficial to cultivate an appreciation for trained language interpreters. (While the terms *interpreter* and *translator* are often used synonymously, it's important to understand that **a translator interprets written expression, while an interpreter translates oral expression**.)

One of the benefits of interpreters is that they can help clients gain a better understanding of the strategies and interventions you believe would be helpful to them. They can also translate documentation and procedures (e.g., scheduling, reminder calls, etc.), which reduces the inconsistency of services. Trained interpreters may also be able to help reduce the likelihood of microaggressions. For example, there are times when your genuine effort to overcome a language barrier—for example, by writing out desired phrases, translating it word-for-word, and reading the translation—might result in a translation that is different than what you intended. However, an interpreter who understands the nuances of both languages can hear what you are trying to say and can convey that interpretation to your client more accurately.

Limitations of Interpreters

Building Rapport

While trained interpreters can be very beneficial in assisting you in your efforts to serve others, they have some limitations as well. One limitation is that it can be difficult to build rapport with your client through an interpreter. When working with interpreters, helping professionals often don't know whether they should look at and focus their attention on the client (who is speaking a foreign language) or the interpreter (through whom understandable communication will come).

Some argue that looking at the client may risk appearing disingenuous, as the professional is trying to nonverbally communicate sincerity and value for what the client is saying when both know that the professional cannot understand what is being said. However, others believe that not looking at the client has the potential to unintentionally convey to the client that they are not respected, valued, or important enough to be looked at. Therefore, many interpreters encourage helping professionals to focus their attention on the client, while also encouraging the client to direct their answers to the helping professional. This allows the interpreter to be a helpful language tool while significantly reducing the blurring of roles as a part of the professional dynamic.

YOU UNDERSTOOD ME THE WHOLE TIME?

Consider... a client I had the pleasure of working with who was a mother of a large family. Because the family primarily spoke Russian in the home, I arranged an interpreter to assist. Having a particular appreciation for showing value and respect to build rapport, I asked my questions to the mother directly. As I did, she listened intently, also looking directly at me as I spoke, and then waited for the interpreter to provide the Russian explanation of what I had said.

As I began to wrap up, I asked about the difference between one of the children's behaviors at school versus at home. Before the interpreter could translate, the mother answered me in English by expressing, "He's good at school. His teachers love him. But at home, he's always angry." It was reassuring to look over and see that the interpreter was just as shocked as I was. I expressed my pleasant surprise that she understood my question and then followed up by politely asking, "So you could understand me the entire time?" She explained that she only knew a little English, but that particular question was one she had been asked multiple times from other professionals and thus felt comfortable enough to answer in English. This experience validated my nonverbal efforts to build rapport with her, which allowed her to feel comfortable enough to risk sharing verbally with me without fear of judgment.

Difficulty Reading between the Lines

Another challenge when working with interpreters is that they may have difficulty reading between the lines. Just as there are verbal and nonverbal forms of communication that can be sources of valuable understanding, we can also glean information from what the client says *directly*, as well as from what they *indirectly* imply with their words. When you are dependent on an interpreter to relay what a client is trying to say, it can be beneficial to let the interpreter know that you would appreciate as much context and meaning as possible to help you understand the client's intended meaning. Since not all interpreters are equal, their ability to do this to your satisfaction may be a determining factor in which interpreter services you utilize.

Conveying More (or Less) than What Is Intended

Similar to the difficulty of reading between the lines, there may be times when an interpreter conveys more (or less) than you or your client intended to convey. This is one reason why it is beneficial to build a healthy professional relationship with an interpreter so you can discuss how much detail versus summary you would prefer. Some helping professionals who frequently utilize interpreter services recommend requesting the same interpreter over and over again to help build continuity in services provided and understanding conveyed.

THAT'S NOT WHAT SHE SAID!

Consider... an adult female client I had met for the first time, whose primary language was Spanish and who required the use of an interpreter. During our first session, I made intentional efforts to speak clearly and to wait patiently for the interpretation of my client's responses. As the session went on, even though I didn't understand the Spanish words being spoken, I began to pick up on the client's nonverbal communication (e.g., facial expressions and body posture), as well as the emotional intensity of certain responses. This made me even more eager to hear the interpretation that matched those expressions. It is for this reason that a particular exchange unsettled me.

I had asked a question about whether the client had experienced any struggles in her marital relationship. Her reply was the most animated of her responses, which included almost 30 seconds of intense facial expressions, a variety of up and down emotions, and changes in body position. She seemed like she wanted to say more but stopped herself because she realized she was about to give me a long story when I only asked her a yes or no question. I found myself sitting on the edge of my seat as I waited to find out what hornet's nest of insight I had just uncovered. However, when the interpreter spoke, she said, "She said, 'No.'" In my mind I wanted to scream, "She said more than that! Tell me what she really said!"

Instead, I forced myself to consider the possibility that this interpreter had worked with previous professionals who preferred short summaries and only the facts rather than "all that extra stuff." I then chose to say, "While I appreciate the effort to provide me with a condensed version, it would be more helpful if you could covey as much as possible about what my client says so I can have a better chance at understanding and learning what she needs." The interpreter rewarded my genuine request with a look of pleasant surprise and followed through on providing the information I needed.

Pros and Cons of Family-Member Interpreters

There are occasions when you might offer to schedule an interpreter, only for your client to respectfully decline because they would like a family member (e.g., a parent, cousin) who speaks multiple languages to assist instead. To some extent, this can have its benefits, as this family member is likely providing an essential service to the rest of the family that allows them to survive and function in society. In addition, it can save your clients money if interpreter service fees aren't included in the cost of treatment. Having a family member interpret for your client can also decrease discomfort since your client already knows and trusts the family member.

Another benefit is that family members can often interpret meaning better than non-family-member interpreters. No matter how knowledgeable an interpreter is about language, it can be difficult to match the benefits of an established relationship in being able to convey meaning. Anyone who has played the game of Taboo° and has been teamed up with an acquaintance (instead of a close friend or family member) can attest to the seemingly unfair advantage that exists when those in close relationships can use nonverbal gestures or shared experiences to communicate more than words could ever convey. In practice, it's the difference between "What she said was..." and "She doesn't really know the word for it, but what Mom is trying to say is..." These nuances are valuable because you never know what morsel of understanding could be the turning point in your effort to help your client more effectively.

While the use of a family-member interpreter may have its benefits, it also has potential drawbacks that are often overlooked. For example, the family member may have to hear or provide information that was otherwise secret, or the client may refuse to share information because they don't want the family member to hear. Another disadvantage is that it can undermine parental authority when a pre-teen or adolescent serves as the interpreter. When children realize that their parents need them to overcome the language barrier, they may feel inclined to use this leverage to influence parental decision making. Similarly, parents who feel afraid or simply ill-equipped to access necessary services on their own may compromise their parenting boundaries so they can maintain their child's language-interpretation services.

In general, the potential benefits of utilizing children as interpreters are outweighed by the potential long-term disadvantages of that experience on the child. As a therapist, you may need to encourage parents to set healthy boundaries with their child, or you may need to empower the child to preserve their childhood as much as possible while not abusing the potential leverage they may have on their parents. When family members, especially children, are called upon to be the designated interpreter, they often lose out on certain freedoms and may begin to resent their parents. For example, they may want to play outside with their friends after completing their homework, but they instead have to stay inside to assist their mother, who has a scheduled in-home health check-up.

HOW ABOUT THAT GAME CONSOLE?

Consider... the mother who requested that her son stay at home to assist with interpreting her in-home health appointment. When she asked her son to help her, he didn't automatically agree to do so. Instead, he asked, "I'm considering staying behind to help, but speaking of helping, I was wondering whether you had considered my request for the latest game console?" Frustrated that her son was negotiating instead of complying, she stated that she had thought about the game console, and the answer was unfortunately no. Her son responded that, due to her answer, his answer was no as well, adding for impact as he walked out the door, "Good luck with that health appointment!"

Having acknowledged the advantages and disadvantages of interpreter services, you should consider the assistance of an interpreter when you and your client do not share the same primary language. It can improve your communication and understanding efforts, and it can significantly enhance the effectiveness of your efforts to help improve your clients' lives. The questions on the next page can help you consider how to best accommodate individuals who speak a different language.

Cultural Competency Journey Reflection

What are the most common non-English languages spoken in my community?

_____

_____

_____

_____

Are there clients in my community who could benefit from my services if I utilized a trained interpreter? Who are they? How could I benefit them by using an interpreter?

_____

_____

_____

_____

How can I (or my organization) accommodate individuals who do not share my primary language (either directly with a modified service or indirectly through prepared referrals)?

_____

_____

_____

_____

Age

According to the U.S. Census Bureau, it is projected that by the year 2030, more than 20 percent of the population will be over the age of 65 (Vespa, Medina, & Armstrong, 2020). Whether or not you consider working with older adults to be your area of expertise, as age demographics in the United States change, helping professionals will need to adapt their services to meet a greater variety of client needs or adjust to a significant reduction in clients they serve.

Who Are You Calling Old?

As people grow older and wrestle with the significance that age will have on their lives, there is often a desire to redefine the language used to describe age, especially for adults 60 years and older. I recommend using a general descriptor such as *older adult* since there is often an aversion to words such as *old*, *elderly*, and *geriatric*. There are also mixed reactions to the word *senior*, as some people express discomfort with the potential implications of the word. Others proudly use the word to describe themselves alongside the discounts they have been looking forward to benefiting from, which use senior as a descriptor. You might even hear someone proudly declare, "60 is the new 50!" or "I'm 60 years *young!*" These sentiments highlight how people may feel differently than what others might assume given their years on this earth.

It is reasonable for people to have preferences such as these given that, for many, age-related terminology can be used to minimize a person's value and worth. This is evident in the increasingly common challenge that individuals face when they are informed they will soon be grandparents. Many grandparents seek alternative monikers to Grandma and Grandpa, such as Nana and Papa, Gigi and Baba, MawMaw and PawPaw, Grams and Gramps, or Gaga and Yaya. Preferences like these may reflect attempts to deny mortality or may reflect discomfort with terms that convey a decline in one's life experience—especially when individuals are looking forward to more life yet to be lived. And there are those who nonetheless maintain the classic monikers of Grandma and Grandpa, ignoring the associations and reclaiming the names they looked forward to living long enough to see.

Maintaining Value Across the Life Span

There is an unfortunate tendency in today's society for people to utilize derogatory statements regarding age that disparage older adults' worth. These statements convey that older adults no longer have the physical or mental ability to offer a significant contribution to society. Those who are younger face similar challenges in that they are often referred to as being "too young" to know anything of value because they have not truly lived yet.

However, these minimizing views have insufficient justification, as there is no consistency regarding what age is too young or too old. For example, professional football players who are over 40 years of age are often derogatorily referred to as grandpas and told to "get off the field and retire already." In contrast, the average age of psychologists is 50 years, despite an increase in younger psychologists and the retirement of older psychologists (Lin et al., 2018). Contrary to the athletic industry, age is often considered an asset in the mental health field, as educational training combined with life experiences can often enhance a therapist's effectiveness. Instead of being expected to retire at age 40, individuals can start their career as a therapist and begin considering retirement after a few more decades of effective service. As helping professionals, we need to make intentional efforts to value the perspectives and contributions of the older and the younger alike.

Providing Reassurance When Your Age Is Challenged

Just as it is beneficial to reassure your client of the value you see in them despite your potential age difference, it is also beneficial to reassure your client of the value you can offer to them if your age difference becomes a point of concern for them. The key in circumstances such as these is to acknowledge the potential validity of their concerns and to provide reassurance that increases the likelihood of relationship growth.

WHAT DO YOU HAVE TO OFFER?

Consider... my experience as a new marriage and family therapist in my early 20s having the opportunity to provide marriage counseling to a couple in their 60s. We were barely into our first session when the husband said, "I don't mean to sound rude, but we're clearly old enough to be your grandparents. What do you have to offer that can be helpful to us?"

On the surface, this could sound like a challenge to my intelligence, education, abilities, and professionalism. Some therapists have even admitted that if it were them, they might have either taken this as a personal attack or interpreted it as a sign of resistance to therapy. Fortunately, I was able to see that this was not intended to be a confrontation or a way out. Rather, it was a genuine desire for reassurance from someone who wanted help but who expected this help to come from someone who was older and had more life experience.

I responded with, "No worries, that doesn't sound rude at all. That is a legitimate concern, especially because I clearly do not have as many years of experience as either of you. I bring the benefits of professional training that has equipped me with tools specifically designed to help couples across the life span. I will do my best to understand you both and to highlight the strategies I believe have the best chance of helping you grow where you desire to grow. I also have the benefit of not being in your relationship, which means that without needing to be wiser or smarter, I have the ability to see and hear things that you might not be able to see or hear. Hopefully, I can help you see things in yourselves and in each other that you can both use to strengthen your relationship. In the end, you'll hopefully leave better off than when you came in, and you won't have had to wait to find someone older to accomplish that. Is that something you're willing to try?"

The husband then responded, "Alright then, let's see what you've got." Having validated the age concern instead of dismissing it, we went on to make great progress together.

The More Things Change, The More They Stay the Same

When evaluating the role that age may play in the services you provide, it is helpful to acknowledge that while older adults often share similar abilities and desires as their younger counterparts, there are also significant cognitive and physiological changes, as well as negative life events, that are unique to older adults. Addressing these concerns may require specialized attention and possibly specialized training. For example, there are certain experiences that most individuals are more likely to go through at an older age, such as death and loss, which people need to experience in order to fully understand them.

WHEN LOSS BECOMES COMMON

Consider... an older adult who is the youngest sibling in a family of ten and who is one of three remaining living siblings. As with most families, the loss of the first sibling was devastating, and the second and third losses were difficult as well, but the family's strong faith helped them successfully navigate the grief process. However, when the fourth and fifth siblings passed, a representative from the family's funeral home called and explained that the youngest sibling had been designated to handle future funeral arrangements. This sibling was told that she had coped better than the other family members with the various losses over the years and had become very experienced in the process of funeral and burial arrangements.

Although no one wants to experience so much loss that funeral and burial arrangements become commonplace, it reflects the experiences that frequently occur with older age. Older adults know what it is like to have developed healthy friendships over a lifetime and to find themselves uncharacteristically lonely as those friends pass away. As helping professionals, whether you have experienced significant loss in your lifetime compared to your client or not, you have the challenge of nonjudgmentally understanding the impact of those experiences (or lack thereof) on your client's perspectives, motivations, and decision making. Even if you don't share their exact experiences, remember to use whatever experiences you have as a starting point to enhance your understanding and empathy for their unique experiences.

The Misconception of Automatic Age Decline

One common misconception regarding age is that older adults always have cognitive and physiological limitations. Similar to how people often treat those with disabilities, younger individuals may address older adults by yelling, "Is there anything I can do for you?!" In response, the older adult is likely to respond, "I'm old, not hard of hearing. You don't need to yell!" I personally love to go to weddings and see grandmothers who are the first ones to get on the dance floor and the last ones to leave. At the same time, many older adults face the reality that they can feel healthy and strong from a mental and emotional standpoint, but they feel frustrated that their body seems to be betraying them by not always working as it did before.

As helping professionals, we should always assume physiological and cognitive competence until we are informed otherwise. It is better to assume that a client is capable and to allow them to share any struggles with dignity and on their own terms, rather than to assume decline and risk needing to overcome a perceived age-related microaggression. One way to avoid minimizing an older adult's abilities and interests is to remember that abilities and interests do not necessarily decline with age. In fact, they often remain strong and can even increase over time.

WE'RE LOOKING FORWARD TO THAT ONE

Consider... my experience as a new marriage and family therapist providing premarital counseling to a couple who were 80 and 82 years of age. Utilizing the PREPARE/ENRICH® relationship assessment, we had some great sessions together, with each session focusing on identifying areas of strength and growth in one or more common areas of relationship struggle.

We had just completed a section on management of finances when I turned the page in my guidebook and saw that the next section was on sex and intimacy. I must have given some type of minimizing nonverbal response because the husband-to-be joyously said, "Don't skip over that section, son. We're looking forward to that one!"

While I like to consider myself to be measured in my degree of emotional expression in therapeutic settings, my shock was clear and unfiltered. In exploring my reaction, I realized that I had no context for sexual activity with older adults. It was as if I subconsciously concluded that interest and ability with regard to an active sex life simply ended after a certain age.

As helping professionals, we need to make intentional efforts to value those who are younger, those who are older, and everyone in between. Just as there are times when being younger has its benefits, there are times when being older is preferable. Time and age alone don't necessarily provide that benefit. Simply existing in this world teaches us little. What matters more are the lessons we have learned from the experiences we have had. I encourage you to learn from your opportunities and to encourage your clients to do the same. The following worksheet can assist you in this process.

Cultural Competency Journey Reflection

In what ways does your age assist in your effort to understand and empathize with others' experiences?

_____

_____

_____

_____

What life experiences do you consider to be difficult to understand and empathize with that may be influenced by your age?

_____

_____

_____

_____

How can you reassure others that, despite your age differences, you can still be of service in helping them improve their lives?

_____

_____

_____

_____

Religion & Spirituality

According to a Pew Research Center study (2017), 84 percent of adults and children around the world are affiliated with a religion, with the remaining 16 percent being unaffiliated (with some identifying as atheist or agnostic). Within the United States, a majority of Americans identify with a religious faith. As helping professionals, we need to be prepared to increase our understanding of the role of faith in the lives of our clients, regardless of whether we hold different beliefs.

Religions in the World

(Pew Research Center, 2017)

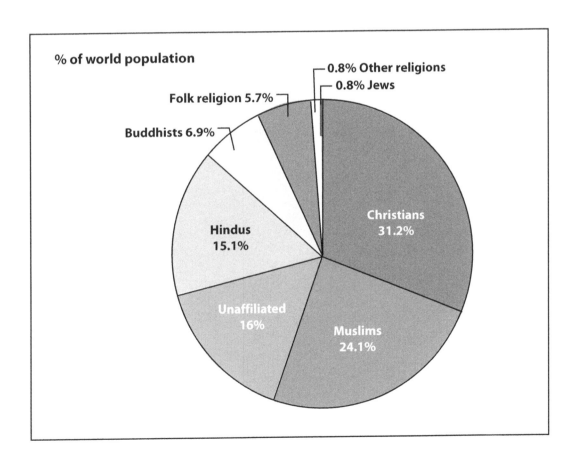

Religions in the United States

(Pew Research Center, 2014)

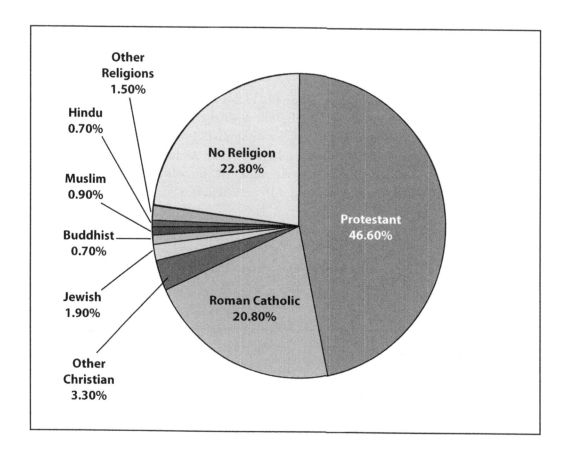

Beyond Tolerance & Coexistence

Many helping professionals who seek to be culturally competent with regard to religion focus their efforts on the common goal of religious tolerance. For example, there are popular bumper stickers that use religious symbols whose shapes spell out words like *tolerance* and *coexist*. For some, these bumper stickers convey the well-known message of "Can't we all just get along?" and encourage an end to oppression and discrimination based on differences in religious beliefs. However, efforts such as these are not universally appreciated. Other people believe these bumper stickers convey a message that the distinctions between religious beliefs are insignificant, as if to say, "We all believe in a higher power, so let's stop fighting and coexist peacefully." Although both perspectives encourage the reduction of discriminatory actions based on religious differences, the latter perspective emphasizes the importance of maintaining distinct faith beliefs.

For the purposes of increasing your cultural competence regarding faith beliefs, you don't need to choose one side of this argument. Rather, it is important to increase your understanding of various perspectives so if a client identifies a preference or discomfort with these types of expressions, you can resist the temptation to sway them to a certain belief. Instead, you can validate the beliefs and the preferences *they* have. This approach goes beyond tolerance and coexistence in that it involves having an appreciation for the significance that various religious beliefs play in people's sense of identity, purpose, and existence.

Assess the Role That Religion Plays in a Client's Life

There are various roles that religion can play in your clients' lives. Many individuals maintain religious beliefs that are a core aspect of their identity, while others have religious beliefs but do not place them as high on their priority list. Still others have no religious beliefs.

Just as with many other aspects of cultural competency growth, it is helpful to first explore the role religion plays in your own life. After you have done so, take the extra step to explore why religion has that role. Were you taught those beliefs in your family of origin? Did you gain an appreciation for your religious beliefs after a significant life experience? Then consider some of the many ways others might have come to hold their religious beliefs. It is more difficult to tell someone how to best express their religious beliefs when you remember that various cultures value and practice religion in different ways. This can be a beneficial practice in empathy that prepares you to support your clients in real life.

Assess the Support a Client Receives for Their Religious Beliefs

When individuals within the same family hold differing religious beliefs, this is often a significant source of emotional distress. This can occur when family members hold conflicting religious beliefs, when family members believe in different doctrines within the same larger religion, or when certain family members have religious affiliations while other family members have none.

When working with clients on issues related to religion and spirituality, it can be helpful to assess whether your client feels supported by their family when it comes to their religious beliefs or whether these beliefs have resulted in anguish and separation. Unfortunately, some people may begin to hide their religious beliefs when they anticipate a lack of family support. And depending on the degree to which an individual considers religion to be a core aspect of their identity, it may feel to them that in hiding their beliefs, they are hiding themselves from the people they long to be closest to.

Supporting the Client ≠ Supporting Their Beliefs

A common barrier with helping professionals is the belief that supporting the client in their religious beliefs feels the same as supporting the client's religious beliefs. This is especially significant when helping professionals and their clients do not share the same faith beliefs. While this is a legitimate concern, it is possible to support your client in their beliefs without promoting or endorsing their religious beliefs. The emphasis here is on supporting your client in making healthy life decisions, even if their decisions are not what you would have chosen if you were in their shoes.

A FAMILY FAITH DILEMMA

Consider... a young man in his 20s who seeks out counseling for a family faith dilemma. His family is from Thailand, a country where Buddhism is the most prominent religion, and his parents identify strongly with Buddhism and have raised him to share their religious beliefs. Although the client was born in Thailand, his family moved to the United States when he was very young, resulting in an acculturation process where he learned certain cultural values within his home, while being exposed to other values outside the home. Over time, he gained an appreciation for the Christian faith. Foreseeing the potential implications this would have on his family, he seeks the support of a Christian therapist instead of a spiritual advisor.

Although therapists are usually known for being neutral, a Christian therapist may have an easier time appearing neutral to this client while finding subtle ways to lean him toward Christian preferences. However, in doing so, the therapist would not truly be helping the client accomplish his goals. By leading the client in this prescribed direction, the client won't learn how to make significant life decisions for himself. Instead, the best treatment course would be to help this client explore the pros and cons of his choices, including the implications of these choices on his family and on his own life, as well as the degree to which he would have regrets with regard to either choice.

When it comes to religious beliefs and values, we need to make every effort to avoid converting clients to our personal beliefs and to instead guide them toward a healthier life in a way that is personalized for them. When you are equipped with increased self-awareness and are confident in your own beliefs, you can successfully cultivate a degree of support that transcends differing beliefs between you and your clients and can help them make the best decisions possible for their lives. Use the worksheet on the next page to explore the role of religion in your life and to examine how you can increase your ability to serve clients who hold different beliefs than you.

Cultural Competency Journey Reflection

How significant of a role, if any, does religion play in my life?

_____

_____

_____

_____

What type of support, or lack thereof, do I receive from family and friends regarding my faith beliefs?

_____

_____

_____

_____

What opportunities do I have to learn more about and gain a greater appreciation for other religious beliefs?

_____

_____

_____

_____

Final Thoughts

As I conclude my overview of multicultural awareness and diversity, I'd like to remind you of a few key guiding principles to support you in your efforts to increase your cultural competency as a helping professional. Accept what you don't know. Value what you do know. Learn more. These principles can guide you through every new cultural learning opportunity you encounter.

Remember that multicultural competence is a journey, not a destination. It's less about whether you know as much as someone else and more about your willingness to learn more as you have opportunities to do so.

On behalf of every client you will have the opportunity to serve, thank you for investing in your ever-increasing cultural competency and, ultimately, in your ability to be more effective in helping others feel seen and supported in their life journey.

Cultural Competency Journey Reflection

What immediate changes can I make in my daily professional life (through my thoughts or my actions) to be more culturally aware and considerate?

_____

_____

_____

_____

What opportunities do I have to put those considerations into practice?

_____

_____

_____

_____

What concerns remain that might keep me from implementing these considerations? What insights from this book might help me overcome those concerns and initiate changes that can positively impact my cross-cultural professional relationships?

_____

_____

_____

_____

References

For your convenience, purchasers can download and print
the worksheets from www.pesi.com/Lambers

American Psychiatric Association. (2013). *Diagnostic and statistical manual of mental disorders* (5th ed.). https://doi.org/10.1176/appi.books.9780890425596

Atkinson, D. R., Morten, G., & Sue, D. W. (Eds.). (1993). *Counseling American minorities: A cross-cultural perspective* (4th ed.). Brown & Benchmark.

Berry, J. W. (1980). Acculturation as varieties of adaptation. In A. M. Padilla (Ed.), *Acculturation: Theory, models, and some new findings* (pp. 9–25). Westview Press.

Brault, M. W. (2012, July). *Americans with disabilities: 2010.* United States Census Bureau. https://www2.census.gov/library/publications/2012/demo/p70-131.pdf

Carney, C. G., & Kahn, K. B. (1984). Building competencies for effective cross-cultural counseling: A developmental view. *The Counseling Psychologist, 12*(1), 111–119.

Clark, K., & Clark, M. (1941/1958). Racial identification and preference in Negro children. (Unpublished study made possible by a grant from Julius Rosenwald Fund, 1940–1941). In Maccoby, E. E., Newcomb, T. M., & Hartley, E. L. (Eds.), *Readings in Social Psychology* (pp. 602–611). Holt Reinhard.

Colby, S. L., & Ortman, J. M. (2015, March). *Projections of the size and composition of the U.S. population: 2014 to 2060.* United States Census Bureau. https://www.census.gov/content/dam/Census/library/publications/2015/demo/p25-1143.pdf

Coleman, H. L. K. (1998). General and multicultural counseling competency: Apples and oranges? *Journal of Multicultural Counseling and Development, 26*(3), 147–156.

D'Andrea, M., Daniels, J., & Heck, R. (1991). Evaluating the impact of multicultural counseling training. *Journal of Counseling and Development, 70*(1), 143–150.

Falchuk, B. (Writer), & McCrane, P. (Director). (2015). Jagged little tapestry [Television series episode]. In I. Brennan et al. (Producers), *Glee.* Brad Falchuk Teley-Vision, Ryan Murphy Productions, & 20th Century Fox Television.

Gurrentz, B. (2018, November 15). *Living with an unmarried partner now common for young adults.* United States Census Bureau. https://www.census.gov/library/stories/2018/11/cohabitaiton-is-up-marriage-is-down-for-young-adults.html

Hardy, K. V., & Laszloffy, T. A. (1995). The cultural genogram: Key to training culturally competent family therapists. *Journal of Marital & Family Therapy, 21*(3), 227–237.

He, W., Goodkind, D., & Kowal, P. (2016, March). *An aging world: 2015.* United States Census Bureau. https://www.census.gov/content/dam/Census/library/publications/2016/demo/p95-16-1.pdf

Johns Hopkins Bloomberg School of Public Health. (n.d.). *Diversity wheel*. https://www. jhsph.edu/about/school-wide-initiatives/diversity-and-inclusion/resources

Jones, J. M. (2021, February 24). *LGBT identification rises to 5.6% in latest U.S. estimate*. Gallup. https://news.gallup.com/poll/329708/lgbt-identification-rises-latest-estimate.aspx

Lin, L., Stamm, K., & Christidis, P. (2018). The U.S. psychology workforce is getting younger. *Monitor on Psychology, 49*(7), 21.

Livingston, G., & Brown, A. (2017, May 18). Intermarriage in the U.S. 50 years after Loving v. Virginia. Pew Research Center. http://www.pewsocialtrends.org/2017/05/18/intermarriage-in-the-u-s-50-years-after-loving-v-virginia

Loveless, T. (2017, March). *The 2017 Brown Center Report on American education: How well are American students learning?* The Brookings Institution. https://www.brookings.edu/wp-content/uploads/2017/03/2017-brown-center-report-on-american-education.pdf

McIntosh, P. (1988). White privilege: Unpacking the invisible knapsack. *Independent School, 49*(2), 31–35.

Michigan Roundtable for Diversity and Inclusion. (2010, November 4). *Tim Wise—Guilt or responsibility* [Video]. YouTube. https://www.youtube.com/watch?v=XhOh_EGe41Y&feature=youtu.be

Newport, F. (2013, July 25). *In U.S., 87% approve of black-white marriage, vs. 4% in 1958*. Gallup. http://news.gallup.com/poll/163697/approve-marriage-blacks-whites.aspx

PayScale. (2019, April 2). *Gender pay gap statistics for 2019*. https://www.payscale.com/data/gender-pay-gap

Pew Research Center. (2014). *Religious landscape study*. https://www.pewforum.org/religious-landscape-study/

Pew Research Center. (2016, October 26). *One-in-five U.S. adults were raised in interfaith homes*. https://www.pewforum.org/2016/10/26/religion-in-marriages-and-families

Pew Research Center. (2017, April 5). *The changing global religious landscape*. https://www.pewforum.org/2017/04/05/the-changing-global-religious-landscape/

PFLAG. (2021, January). *PFLAG national glossary of terms*. https://pflag.org/glossary

Pioneer Press. (2015, October 28). *Hundreds rally in Black Lives Matter protest at State Fair*. https://www.twincities.com/2015/08/28/hundreds-rally-in-black-lives-matter-protest-at-state-fair

Ponterotto, J. G., Fuertes, J. N., & Chen, E. C. (2000). Models of multicultural counseling. In S. D. Brown & R. W. Lent (Eds.), *Handbook of counseling psychology* (3rd ed.) (pp. 639–669). John Wiley & Sons.

Priest, R. (1994). Minority supervisor and majority supervisee: Another perspective of clinical reality. *Counselor Education and Supervision, 34*(2), 152–158.

Rogers, C. (1959). A theory of therapy, personality and interpersonal relationships as developed in the client-centered framework. In S. Koch (Ed.), *Psychology: A study of a science, Vol. 3: Formulations of the person and the social context* (pp. 185–256). McGraw Hill.

Sabnani, H. B., Ponterotto, J. G., & Borodovsky, L. G. (1991). White racial identity development and cross-cultural counselor training: A stage model. *The Counseling Psychologist, 19*(1), 76–102.

Sue, D. W., & Sue, D. (2013). *Counseling the culturally diverse: Theory and practice* (6th ed.). John Wiley & Sons.

Underwood, S. (Co-host). (2016, September 20). (Season 7, Episode 7). [TV series episode]. In S. Gilbert & J. Redmann (Executive Producers), *The Talk*. CBS Productions.

United States Government Accountability Office. (2018, March). *K-12 education: Discipline disparities for Black students, boys, and students with disabilities.* https://www.gao.gov/assets/700/690828.pdf

Vanorman, A., & Jacobsen, L. A. (2020, February 12). *U.S. household composition shifts as the population grows older; more young adults live with parents.* Population Reference Bureau. https://www.prb.org/u-s-household-composition-shifts-as-the-population-grows-older-more-young-adults-live-with-parents/

Vespa, J., Medina, L., & Armstrong, D. M. (2020, February). *Demographic turning points for the United States: Population projections for 2020 to 2060.* United States Census Bureau. https://www.census.gov/content/dam/Census/library/publications/2020/demo/p25-1144.pdf

Zalman, M. (2012). Qualitatively estimating the incidence of wrongful convictions. *Criminal Justice Bulletin, 48*(2), 221–279.

Made in the USA
Monee, IL
23 January 2023

25990324R00131